# BEHOLD
## *What Is*
## GREATER THAN THYSELF

## AND OTHER SURF STORIES

*by*
*Chris Ahrens*

**With Illustrations by Wade Koniakowsky**

Cover art and illustrations by Wade Koniakowsky
Website: http://www.koniakowsky.com/
Editorial and production services provided by Roy Latas

ISBN # 978-0-9640858-7-9
Printed in the United States of America
First Edition

Behold what is greater than thyself.

*- Levana*

*To Yummy Tiger, Lucas Tiger, Marley Tiger, Clelia and Craig.*

With special thanks to: Wade Koniakowsky, Karen Wilson, Reed Rindge, Michael Cassidy, Hagan Kelley, Stuart Grauer, Lori Gertz, Erik Johnson, Robin Colvey, Roy Latas, T-Roc, Tracy Ahrens, Tiffany Anderson, Corporate Color Printing and my spiritual advisors, Bruce and Claudia De Soto.

# CONTENTS

**_Behold What Is Greater Than Thyself_**

# Chapter 1

# TOMMY

*There are many ways to live in Baja and at least as many ways to die. If you miss being gunned down by bandits, cops, or drug cartels, you might get bitten by a poisonous Mexican spider, fanged by an angry Mexican rattlesnake, or devoured by an international shark. A sort of Devil's Triangle West, nothing behaves correctly once the border is crossed. Small planes fall from a clear sky, pleasure boats are found bobbing mid-ocean without a crew, and the carcasses of new SUV's form rusty roadside grave markers. Don't drink the water. Don't swallow the worm. Don't flash your cash.*

*Still, for everyone that finds Baja hell on earth, someone else considers it the world's last paradise. For surfers it's a great place to find lonely and perfect waves. For sinners it's a good place to become a saint. For saints, it's a convenient place to become a sinner. While the unlucky can lose their wallets, their health and their sanity in twenty-four hours or less, the chosen ones part only with things not worth keeping. Baja is a bad place for some, a good place for others and the only place for a young surfer in big trouble.*

**Baseball is a game. Football is a sport. Surfing is a disease.**
*–Anonymous*

He was not thinking about Baja as he celebrated his 15th birthday by surfing his home break, the Newport River Jetties on a powerful southwest swell that August afternoon in 2005. A thick green wedge of a wave, well overhead, stood up on the sandbar, and the kid was there to meet it, spinning around at just the right moment, no paddle, free falling into the pit, disappearing deep within the tube and exiting, hands stylishly at the sides to the hoots of those who witnessed the miracle of another perfect ride.

# Behold

Tommy Stern was like a battery operated toy—moving only when the switch was flicked, which for him required submersion in saltwater. He had been among the best surfers in Newport Beach, California; some would say the world for over a year now. He stood the same height as the board he rode that day, 5"6", was square shouldered, tightly muscled, deeply tanned, with shaggy naturally dark-brown hair whose tips were burnt to white straw by the sun. His menacing scowl was almost handsome in an evil sort of way. Girls were attracted to him in spite of his ragged appearance and often attempted to ease his pain. Whenever he smiled, something he did only when he wanted a favor, the opposite sex found him irresistible. Everybody liked Tommy, and Tommy liked nobody. Some he actually hated. Topping that list was his father, Big Tom.

In just one decade Big Tom had gone from rock-solid surf hero to a creature too weak and flabby to paddle a surfboard. From the time his boy could walk, Big Tom made his boards and took him to nearly every West Coast surf spot. That was before faith had died along with Big Tom's wife and Tommy's mother, Ellen. She was a saint, a tender flower destroyed as it reached toward an angry sun. A second sort of cancer, a disease of the soul, steadily ate away the survivors' insides until they were hollowed out like some spiritless jack-o-lantern. But being spiritless mattered little to Tommy. In fact little mattered to him. Besides, he did just fine as a loner in a town he alone saw the diseased underbelly of.

He had been called thief, but to him taking from these "useful fools," wasn't stealing but gathering a portion of what should have been his all along. Besides, he would use the cash in better ways than those "one man at a time prostitutes," as he called the women who had hitched their fortunes to the bank accounts of what he imagined were nothing but fat old men. He was unsure what was worse–the men working for the reward of their first heart attack or the women who hoped to cash in, patiently waiting with their feet bound like three-inch lotuses to more shoes than fifty of them could wear in a lifetime. This thinking made it easy for Tommy to break into cars, enter unlocked bedroom windows and tear women's purses from their bejeweled fingers. There was no rehab for a kid addicted to the rocket fuel of entitlement and adrenalin.

He strolled with his board beneath his arm in the fading light of the brilliant sunset with no idea that the next twenty-four hours would change everything, including his name, his family status and the place he lived, which would be the aforementioned Baja Peninsula that awaited him 108 well-paved miles to the south.

Behold

# Chapter 2

# REQUIEM FOR A SURFER

*In the U.S. young surfers were once called "gremmies." After the Australian surf invasion of the mid '70s rearranged everything in American surf culture, including our language, these same kids were called "grommets." By any name, young, sun ripened, bad mannered surfers who eternally arrive at beaches to prove themselves in order to be allowed into the ranks of their elders have to pass a brutal initiation. This unofficial rite of passage is performed daily on the California coast or anywhere else in the world with a longtime surfing population.*

Tommy's precocious surfing style and quiet disposition worked in his favor since loud gremmies got strapped to the roofs of cars, locked into their trunks, taped to lifeguard towers, or simply drenched in corn syrup, rolled in the sand, sun dried until crispy and sacrificed to the sea, where they sank or swam. Many gremmies don't survive the years of pain and humiliation and find easier, safer sports than surfing from which to launch into adulthood. Survivors are rewarded with knowing they can handle their peers, the ocean, and the pleasure of torturing those who come after them. Tommy was not considered a gremmie for long, if at all. In fact he couldn't ever remember being called that name.

He had no more memory of his first time surfing than he did his first baby steps. He thought of his first surfboard the way another child would a swing set. Surfing began as a game you played when you were a toddler. By third grade, right after his mother's death, he put away childish games and began riding waves in earnest, staying in the surf long after other kids had left the water to nap in their parent's beachfront homes, the cabins of their yachts, or on the couches of luxurious RV's, all stuffed and softened on gourmet dreams.

In contrast, Tommy went through the wonder years lean and hungry, paddling out through mountains of whitewater, learning to negotiate dangerous riptides, slicing his feet open on jagged rocks, being pierced repeatedly by sea urchins, stung by stingrays and several times encountering big sharks. Not even a huge predator could make the kid leave the water, however. While others his age surfed for a few years, surfing was more than an adolescent sport for Tommy. This was his identity, his drug, his life.

At first he made progress with great difficulty, then, as the ocean unlocked her secrets, things became easier. While never really a gremmie, Tommy was always a rebel. His rebellion was totally self-centered and struck against everything in his way. He was not the typical SoCal rebel in that he never touched cigarettes or drugs because he figured they would interfere with his surfing. He hated even the scent of alcohol, because it had murdered his father's soul. The boy, however, kept himself intoxicated through the unpredictable rush and acceleration the ocean offered, often riding waves until his arms and legs no longer functioned.

Now, on his birthday, the ocean itself presented a gift in the form of a tide so low you could nearly walk with dry feet out to the peak on sand as hard as concrete. With delight he heard the pounding wedges fall like so many pounds of block ice onto a concrete floor. The morning sky appeared like a metallic ceiling contrasted by glass laid out all the way to the sun. Paddling out he could see what few others saw—not just the deep holes in the ocean, caverns called tubes or barrels—but a vision that revealed his immediate future, knowing that those barrels would soon be his living room—a safe and comfortable place to find shelter. A few dozen others joined him in the surf, and he enjoyed silently crushing their egos through his superior ability. Around noon he left the water for a hamburger and fries at the grill across the street on Coast Highway. On his way back to the beach, he followed his usual program and without emotion stole an unattended purse from a foolishly unlocked car. After hiding the purse in the jetty's rocks, he casually returned to his birthday wave feast and didn't leave the water until sunset. Even then it was difficult to walk away from the last remnants of spitting top to bottom tubes.

Before walking home, he gathered the purse from the rocks and hid it in his towel. He didn't show his annoyance when approached by three sunburnt gremmies, laughing, shouting, and kicking sand on each other on their ways home. They chased each other with their tiny boards and secretly hoped Tommy would acknowledge them–all giddy at seeing their hero who was only a year or two older than they. Realizing Tommy wouldn't approve, one of the kids dropped the cigarette he was smoking into the sand. They adored him, but he thought of them as parasites, pathetic children playing kiddy games while he considered himself a man of conviction and accomplishment, hardened like the sand bottom at River Jetties and the unforgiving world surrounding it. Nodding to the gremmies, he passed them and moved on.

As he walked he recalled the day he graduated from the splash zone these kids would be forever stuck in. It had been double overhead-plus at the Jetties with violent riptides forming rivers that churned back out to sea. There was no fighting this river, and earlier that week two people had drowned attempting to do so. Many of the older guys had excuses for staying on the beach that day. But here was a twelve-year-old child in a too-large wetsuit, carrying his board in licorice lace arms toward the foreboding lineup. He knew the rip would take him out without a struggle and he threw himself into it without a thought. Once in the lineup, he noticed the telltale signs of fear coming from some of the men–talking too much, or laughing nervously while awaiting the next big set.

One of the men ordered Tommy to paddle in before the set arrived. Tommy didn't reply, but simply paddled further out into deeper water, where he sat quietly alone. When the next set appeared everyone but Tommy scratched for the horizon. Those who didn't make it over the first wave were driven back to shore where they sat out the remainder of the afternoon in shame and silence. Everyone but Tommy tried to avoid the biggest waves. He was not running anywhere. Instead, he stroked into the wave. Fluttering at the top for a moment, he felt the world give way beneath him as he dropped to the bottom and managed a shaky turn on legs too weak to hold against the Pacific as it collapsed on him. His leash snapped on impact and sent his board tumbling to shore alone. In an instant he was pushed down and pinned to the sand. His lungs were bursting for air when he recalled how his uncle, who had once ditched his small plane in the ocean, told him that breathing water would make drowning easier. Was he drowning? He had been spun so violently that when he began swimming, he collided again with the ocean's floor. Finally surrendering, he breathed in saltwater and tricked his lungs into believing it was air—cool and relaxing. When he finally drifted back to the surface he gasped for life and spat out the water in his lungs before the next wave descended upon him and took him to the bottom again. Nobody was swimming out to help him. He floated to the surface, in a daze, cleared his head enough to avoid drowning and followed his board's route to the beach while subsequent waves buried him. After retrieving his board from the rip, he caught a wave that contained more sand than water in the violent shore break. He was slammed hard before being deposited on the beach and rolled like a log until finding enough strength to rise to his feet. Once on the dry sand, people came forward offering towels and congratulations to the kid for surviving the bomb.

To their surprise, he didn't acknowledge them or their words of praise and caution, instead paddling back out and repeating the process three more times, twice taking brutal wipeouts, once colliding with his board, bruising for sure, and maybe breaking some ribs. But he did not give up until he dropped in on the biggest wave of the day, was swallowed by whitewater and surfaced to see the two halves of his broken board being tossed to shore like a child's toy. That wave, which seemed to have broken a lifetime ago, proved a dividing line in his life, and since then nothing the ocean threw at him scared him. The ocean was his only friend now, and he drew from that well for strength and courage rather than having it rob him of it.

Having no idea what true happiness was, he never realized how far he was from it. He continued walking toward home, pocketing the twenty-dollar bill from the purse and tossing the remaining contents–a license, two credit cards, lipstick and pictures of kids in the gutter. Home, one of the most cherished words in the English language, for Tommy consisted of the most broken down trailer on the coast shared with the most broken down individual he had ever known. While the place did have the advantage of being a block from the beach, it was, at best, a roof.

What would he find there this time? Unwilling to find out immediately, he thought he'd stop by The Frog House, the surf shop on Coast Highway, a few blocks from the trailer. There he would see the owner, TK, who was his closest thing to a friend, a man who had kept him in wetsuits and boards ever since his dad had quit on life years earlier. Maybe there would be a birthday present in the bargain, maybe a set of new clothes. But the shop was locked, and no amount of pounding or shaking the heavy door could change that.

While some of the big surfwear companies had offered Tommy a family man's salary if he signed with them, his soulful ethics wouldn't allow him to become a sponsored contest surfer. You see Tommy was a rare commodity in 2005, what the magazines called a soul surfer, one who rode for the pure pleasure of it, nothing else. And surfing was such a pleasure that he didn't want to contaminate it by making money on it or decorating it with what he saw as the ugly trappings of fame and ego. The pros could keep the gaudy trophies, the groupies, and the endless vacations. He wanted to ride alone, as far as possible from the frantic pilgrims that worshiped at the shrine erected annually to the pros at Huntington Beach. His trophy was no trophy at all, just a belief that he could succeed as a pro surfer if only he would lick the boots of the corporate sponsors that held the purse strings. He either felt that sincerely or was too frightened to actually prove himself on the world's stage. Being young and untried, he was sure of his creed, and he shook TK's door.

Somehow it was different with TK, and he never minded taking the things he offered. In exchange for them he had pasted the surf shop's sticker onto the nose of his board and could see the obvious value in getting that name published in the surf magazines. Peering into the shop, he saw nothing. TK was his final hope for a place to crash if things got heavy at home, which they probably would.

Darkness moved in as he moved out, dread filling each of the few hundred steps required to reach his front door. Big Tom would be half drunk and well on his way fully drunk and totally mean, ready to break anything smaller than himself by the time the boy showed his face. Just last week, the old man had busted the 5'8" flyer shaped by his hero, Richie Collins, over his boy's back. Hardened to the elements by such abuse, he barely noticed the sting of the cold gravel now as it pushed into his bare feet while an unseen dog threatened not far away. When the muscular Rottweiler sprang from the darkness and snapped at him, Tommy smacked it hard with his surfboard, and it yelped before limping back into the shadows.

Maybe if he killed time doing something, anything, Big Tom would be passed out and snoring in his recliner when he arrived. If only TK had been around. Now there was no avoiding a confrontation, and the boy arrived just in time to see the outline of his old man, full glass in hand, teetering like a bear ready to destroy whatever came through that aluminum door.

In the dark, on the trailer's porch, Tommy changed from his wetsuit into dry clothes, opened the door quietly and tiptoed in. The old man greeted him with bloodshot teary eyes as he hugged the still wet kid. Dad had cleared a place on the table for the little celebration centered on the day-old chocolate cake, which was barely larger than a cupcake. Everything smelled of cheap whiskey and cigarettes, one with an inch-long ash, dangled from Big Tom's ashtray as he croaked and coughed his way through happy birthday. It would have been nice, but the boy knew what sorts of presents would follow. They would arrive in rapid succession: happiness, sentimentality, restlessness, sadness, resentfulness, rage, violence.

Lighting the candles from his smoke, Big Tom also managed to catch the tablecloth on fire before the boy patted the little flame out with a damp dishtowel. Now Big Tom, hurt feelings exploding everywhere, skipped all the usual stages and went straight to rage, approaching violence, shouting, "What's the matter boy, my cake's not good enough for you?" With one swoop of a big hand, he cleared the table of everything, including the cake, which was smashed up against the wall. The big man used the momentum in his powerful arm to knock his son to the floor. When the kid got up, Big Tom pushed him again, stunned to find that he did not fly across the room as he used to.

He was stronger now, sturdy and able to hold his ground against an attack. Tommy backed away and stood firm when Big Tom charged, head down toward his target in a rage meant to transfer all those years of damaged feelings. But the boy was quick as sobriety and moved to one side as the bear, conquered by his own momentum kept moving, stumbling, and finally crashing into the thin wooden veneer wall, in which he put a hole the size of his head. Tommy gingerly moved the ten feet from the front room to the little kitchen as his father pulled himself up, rose to full height and prepared to charge again.

As the man stormed forward, there was murder in his red eyes. Tommy defensively grabbed the nearest object, a still warm, greasy cast iron skillet from the stove that he white knuckled until he was close enough to smell all the destruction the whiskey soaked beast possessed. He swung the skillet like a bat, connecting with the flat skull as a dull thud stopped the bear immediately sending it to the ground with nothing to break the fall. Had it not been tragic, it would have been comical the way the bear fell–like a cartoon character–stiff legged, face down. Dead.

At first Tommy felt relief. When panic set in, he paced jerkily like a caged animal. As he looked down at the fallen giant nothing stirred in him except the idea of self-protection. He thought to call the police. Then, recalling his criminal record, twice sentenced to juvenile hall for breaking and entering, once for fighting, he decided against the call. What would he say anyway; that he had killed his own father? No, he would run, maybe all the way to Mexico. Flashes of waves in Baja suddenly flooded his confused thinking.

He had been to Baja a few times and was attracted to the waves and the clean sparseness of the place. That was long ago with his father, when his father was still a man, before alcohol had turned him into a stupid beast. The bear was dead for sure as proven by it remaining still even when his son rifled through his pant's pockets, opening his wallet, discarding it and the welfare check before grasping the twenty, the ten and the seven ones. Thirty-seven dollars, all the old man was worth. There was also some loose change on the sink that Tommy swept into his hand and stuffed into his pockets along with the bills. He forced two changes of clothing into his backpack, crammed his still soaked wetsuit into a plastic garbage bag, lifted the biggest board from his quiver–the 6'10" California semi gun, and ran for the street. He inadvertently left the door wide open, something that would hasten the discovery of the corpse. All Tommy knew was that he had to get out of there, quickly, to Mexico, to anywhere. He ran to the street and while crossing it fell on the asphalt, adrenaline numbing the pain as blood caked quickly on the hard cloth of the shredded knees of his jeans. Recovering, he continued running in the dark, to the stoplight at Orange Street on Coast Highway. Through death he had found life. But he had no idea where that life would lead.

# SOUTH FACING

*The Baja Peninsula is a 775-mile finger of rock and sand painted primarily in various shades of brown, white and blue, defined as much by water as earth. Separated from Mainland Mexico by the Gulf of California, it was once thought to be an island populated entirely by women and ruled by the black queen, Califia from whence Baja (Lower) California, and Alta (Upper) California get their names. We now know that Baja is a peninsula occupied primarily by males.*

Once on Coast Highway, Tommy slipped into the shadows each time he saw a pair of tightly focused headlights, something that convinced his paranoid mind the vehicle belonged to a cop. He thought of returning to the trailer to see if his father had somehow survived. Maybe he should call an ambulance? Recalling the lifeless corpse, however, he knew the old man would not revive. If he felt any remorse, it was buried beneath concern for his own neck. It took over an hour for anyone to stop and pick up the hitchhiking kid. The driver was a religious man with dyed black hair combed over his guilty bald spot, a stiff tan suit with matching tie and a big Bible on the seat. The man's loud voice competed with the radio that was up all the way.

Tommy sat quietly, distracted by thoughts of his capital crime as the religious radio show condemned him to recall words from long ago—*Thou shalt not kill, Thou shalt not steal, Thou shalt honor thy father and mother*—Sunday school mantras that held no comfort. The boy perked up a little to hear the ex pro surfer speak on the radio about how he had once won the Pipe Masters before finding God. But Tommy knew enough about God to realize there was no such thing. How many times had he prayed for his dad to get sober? How many times had he and the old man himself pleaded with God to the point of tears not to take wife and mother? Then, how many times had Tommy prayed for the old man to die–a prayer that was perhaps answered only an hour ago, producing a blessing or a curse–a life of freedom or life imprisonment? Yeah, all smart people knew there was no God. The driver, therefore, was not a smart person, and Tommy disliked him because of it. When he could not stand the radio competing with the noise in his head any longer, he told the fanatic to pull over and was dropped off just a few miles south of where he began, still confined within the city he could no longer call home, Newport Beach.

The town valued its children by the numbers of houses they would inherit multiplied by square footage and proximity to the beach. Tommy hated the brats from school. He knew they were nice to him only because he surfed better than them. He tolerated what he saw as their ignorance, their weakness, their chronic weed smoking, and, in rare cases fake piety. But he could never befriend them. They were gone as soon as life got interesting or difficult, retreating to the isolation of their sterile drywall castles. Still, he somehow knew they were just as underprivileged as he. While they would not admit it even to themselves, many of them were dying from a lack of any family connection. Why else were so many of them addicted to deadly vices in a place that had it all?

As for school itself, he hated it in a way reserved for the truly intelligent. Last year he had enjoyed a literature class where he read Hemingway, Faulkner and Steinbeck. When the teacher suggested Tom Wolfe's *The Pumphouse Gang* he tried that also. He quickly noted that the man named among America's top journalists had gotten everything wrong. Attempting to describe surfing, he called a *kickout* a kickup and a *section* a suction. Contrary to Wolfe's version of the story, the drowned body of surfer Bob Simmons was actually found. Wolfe might be excused for these infractions because he didn't surf, but he even got the words to the Rolling Stones hit "Satisfaction" wrong, misquoting the lead line as "I *ain't* got no satisfaction." Tommy had seen the response to Wolfe's book in the surf magazine where someone had spray painted the words "Tom Wolfe is a Dork," on the Windansea pump house, which was the scene of the crime and the name of the fable. If Tom Wolfe was a dork it followed that so were his forebears–London, Poe, Dickens and all the rest. Tommy's was a fool's wisdom for a teenager worshiping at the altar of his own sheltered opinion.

A car pulled over–this time a new Mercedes. The store-bought cougar allowed the kid to slide the wax of his board onto the plush white leather seats, waiting for her prey to settle in before offering money in trade for him doing disgusting acts. Tommy remained silent, but when they reached the stylish little town of Corona Del Mar, he ordered the woman to pull over to the side of the road. The threat of violence in Tommy's tone, however, did nothing but excite the woman who tore at her blouse until she had ripped out the top two buttons, revealing her enhancement along with a surgically smooth self-assured smile as she drove faster until Tommy shoved his board into her neck, ordering her to the curb. Normally he would have reached over and ripped the big diamond from her ring finger, but considering the circumstances he restrained himself. At curbside, Tommy yanked his board from the car before slamming the door and kicking a dent into it as the pathetic nymphomaniac peeled out into the night. He didn't know or care that she had once been his alma mater's prom queen, praised so long for appearance that she never thought to develop anything else. That evening she had played one of her last cards and was now forced to return to the equally sad creature that had used money as a shield, the creature she called husband, the one that made her miserable life possible.

Tommy stood for several more hours on the side of the road before an old, faded blue VW van pulled over. The van was driven by an older surfer all tanned and happy on his way back home to the wave fertile grounds of San Diego after surfing the long and perfect point waves of Malibu all day on the swell of the season. His big board was strung up neatly inside the van. Beneath the board was a mattress where the surfer had slept on his numerous safaris to Baja,

Tommy silently and correctly guessed.

"I'm Jake Carlson," the man said.

"Tommy Stern," said the kid, holding out his hand without turning to face the man, shaking hands limply before Jake asked, "The Newport Kid? I saw your photo in the mag last month. How did you learn to tube ride like that at your age?" The boy did not reply, but sat lifelessly, staring into the distance. Jake was soon yapping about the waves of K-38, San Miguel, Scorpion Bay and Baja points further south. What the driver took as drug-addled arrogance was anxiety brought on by visions of his dead father combined with exhaustion and that surreal state that accompanies trauma.

Jake offered Tommy a couch to crash on in his one bedroom beach shack in Ocean Beach. Tommy had been to O.B. before with his father on their way to Baja in search of surf. Big Tom called O.B. "the ghetto time forgot" adding that old hippies, bikers and longboarders competed for cheap rent and access to the good waves that lined up on the reefs directly to the south. Little Tommy would laugh in agreement with his dad before they bought a few groceries and continued to Baja.

Tommy accepted Jake's offer and followed him into the little cottage where the older man continued to wonder where the kid had come from, where he was going and what he was doing all alone on the road. He would ask those questions in the morning, and if he didn't get good answers, he would inform the proper authorities.

Jake threw Tommy a blanket, a pillow and a dry towel and showed him where the bathroom and the kitchen were before turning in for the night at around 9:30 that evening. On the couch, the boy dozed off, but didn't really sleep. Each time he closed his eyes he could see his father's dead body before him. *My God, I've killed my own father!* The ghosts arrived as if on parade, burning his skin with bony fingers as one by one they accused him as he lay there, awake or asleep, alive or dead, he was unsure of anything now. The night took a week to pass.

The longboarder, who always woke before dawn to check

the surf at the pier or Sunset Cliffs was up, brewing coffee. Looking around, he saw that the kid was already gone, not caring that his stash of bananas and oranges had disappeared with him, but furious that the silver cup on the mantle, the one he had won at the State Championships at Malibu in 1990 was missing along with all the change on the coffee table. Still, this was a fellow surfer and so, against better judgment, he did not contact the police. Instead he drove his van to the pier, the jetty and other places a young surfer might go. He asked around and nobody had seen a kid matching Tommy's description. By the time he returned home it was past nine. Still reluctant to call the cops, Jake distracted himself with petty projects until eleven o'clock. What he didn't realize was that he had barely missed running into the boy while driving down the same block where Tommy had pawned his trophy. This all took place at a pawnshop a few blocks west of Jake's home, where Tommy received fifty bucks for something priceless to the other surfer.

Jake never did find his prize, and by the time he alerted the cops hours later, Tommy was snug in the bed of a truck beneath piles of carpet and blankets. He had waited in line to illegally cross the border after giving the fifty made on the trophy to a Mexican man he'd met at the Jack in the Box on the U.S. border town of San Ysidro. The man, who did not give his name then, was, at 5'6" no taller than Tommy. His dark, creased skin looked hard as iron, and his grey hair and kind but stern dark eyes signaled that he was a workingman who had suffered for things other than himself. At the border the man was waved across by the *Federales* he had paid off years earlier to assure safe passage in and out of Tijuana. What Tommy didn't realize was that Jose, the man driving the car, was himself a fugitive from the law.

Only three years earlier, Jose had been out fishing when his partner, Joaquin, hooked into a big shark. Jose fought a big fish of his own on the opposite side of the little boat Mexicans called *pangas* as Joaquin reached over the side to gaff the shark. Suddenly the shark made one last run for freedom and in so doing, pulled Joaquin overboard still hanging on to the gaff. The shark swam for deep water, taking down rod and reel along with Joaquin, who continued to clutch the gaff tightly. Releasing his own rod into the water, Jose pulled anchor, started the motor and went after Joaquin. What normally would have been an easy rescue was complicated by the strong current and changing tide. Jose made several passes in the *panga* as the flesh-torn Joaquin made the surface. Each time he got near the struggling Joaquin, he stalled the motor and the current pulled him in the opposite direction. By the time he was in range, Joaquin was lying facedown in a widening mixture of saltwater and his own blood. Jose loaded the broken body on board like a sack of rocks. Unable to revive his partner through numerous rounds of CPR, he radioed shore for help. When Jose arrived at the beach with a dead man, the *Federales* arrested him for the crime of murder, since Mexican law counts a person guilty until proven innocent.

Jose spent six months in a Tijuana penitentiary, where he awaited his murder trial and was a model prisoner, therefore less heavily guarded than normal. One night Jose paid off a guard and slipped out, unnoticed in a laundry truck before hitchhiking back home. Jose had not been tortured, but that would change the next time around. Not everyone survived the torture where a man's private parts could be connected to electrical terminals, or bottles of soda were shaken up and forced into the sinuses. There were even stories of mock executions by firing squad, a man blindfolded while the rifles all fired blanks, leaving the prisoner to wonder if he had died as he cowered for the rest of his life. Solitary confinement could mean being sealed into a steel box in the middle of the yard in temperatures that swelled to well over a hundred outside as inside you were slowly cooked half to death. Jose would die before he went back to that prison.

Tommy's plan was to cross into Baja, head down the coast and make his run for freedom, disappearing forever in the vast expanse of small desert towns. Lying beneath the pile of blankets in the bed of the truck, the boy felt mild relief, but not enough of it to chuckle at the irony that someone would actually be smuggled from the U.S. *into* Mexico.

Jose avoided most of the countless potholes in the old truck whose broken shocks provided no comfort, but jostled Tommy from his bed like a ragdoll whenever he hit a particularly deep hole on the maze that leads past the bars, restaurants and curio shops on *Avenida Revolución* to the steep hill lined with tarpaper and cardboard shacks before dropping back down to Baja's Highway 1, the dangerous and magical ribbon of blacktop that moves monotonously through the desert, just out of sight of bays with water as clear as mountain air, lagoons filled with the cries of newborn whales, and surfers riding mile-long waves. On Baja 1 nothing changes for 745 mind-numbing miles as you try to stay alert, bobbing and weaving through the monotone landscape amid the big trucks, drunk drivers, spaced out cattle and blowing sand, hoping to avoid white line fever, all the way to Cabo San Lucas. When Jose, a fisherman with English far better than Tommy's schoolbook Spanish, pulled over on the highway, he lifted the blankets and cleared a spot for the boy to sit in the cab, a seat he shared with Jose's hyperactive Chihuahua sized mutt, *Pepe*.

"I am Jose Santiago, the grandson of the great man I was named for," said the driver. A thick Mexican accent accompanied his good English as he crossed himself reverently and extended his calloused hand. "Tommy Stern," said the boy, instinctively trusting his future to Jose as they shook hands and Tommy made quick eye contact. Jose was intuitive by nature and everything—the kid's unkempt look, the vacant eyes, the lack of direct visual contact, reminded him of the men in prison, signaling to Jose that the boy was running from the law. But the man asked no questions and gave him back the fifty-dollar bill. Tommy pocketed the money without a word, and Pepe licked the boy's face, something that brought out a long buried childhood, causing the boy to giggle happily in a way he had not done in years.

Tommy slumped back in the cracked leather seat, falling into an apparently dreamless slumber, which was better than his murderer's conscience deserved. His one arm hung out the truck's window while the other was draped around Pepe's neck as they passed boom towns busted from recession, the unseen violence caused by the drug cartels and the sewage pouring unchecked into the once pristine waters and mini Pipeline barrels near Baja Malibu and the Spring Break capitol, Rosarito Beach. But soon the coast fell into a panoramic seascape that ran to the southern and to the western horizon like a floor of glass.

# Chapter 4

# FAMILIA

*A purse seiner is a boat that nets tuna. When a school of tuna is sighted, the net encircles it and traps them. This is an extremely efficient method of fishing, enabling the fleet to eliminate entire schools.*

While to many surfers the bay they were passing is a final destination, to others it is only the beginning–a door, a gateway drug barely hinting at legendary sand points whose names are whispered by insiders, and only published by surfers willing to betray such rugged and delicate beauty for the price of fading surf magazine fame.

Under other circumstances Tommy would have wanted to sample that and other spots, like the four to six foot A-framed peak slamming into the shallow sandbar, fanned clean by offshore winds. As the truck entered the last outpost of civilized mayhem, Ensenada, Tommy continued sleeping. Jose stopped for gas and snacks, before moving beyond town and the little pockets of expatriates and local fishermen whose homes lined the beaches adjacent to a land whose only other inhabitants were wild horses, famished cattle, ranchers, merchants, outlaws and people smart enough to live near the ocean for a fraction of the cost a few miles north. The final obstacle was the military checkpoint where kids with their fingers on M-16 rifles let the truck pass, noting that Jose, who was familiar to them, was driving. Here the coast could breathe freely and miles later a dirt road running at a 45-degree angle migrated back toward the sea on endless washboard of deeply rutted dirt and sand. Even during that hour of bad road Tommy continued sleeping until Jose high-ended the truck and loudly scraped the metallic bottom, tearing out the muffler. The boy woke abruptly to the throaty sound of the unmuffled truck and the sight of a body of water he would learn was called

# Behold

Santa Guadalupe Bay.

Tommy helped rock the truck off the little mound until it was free again. The place smelled of sagebrush and brine mixed with the faint odor of mesquite fires that carried hints of carne asada on light winds. Guadalupe Bay was set in monotone grey now, but an hour earlier it had shown off half a dozen varieties of blue water beneath an orange sky. As if to hide itself from the newcomer, the bay quickly faded to black beneath a new moon.

There were two Guadalupe's, really–the small, humble one near the bay directly before him was inhabited by Jose, his family and about two-dozen equally tightknit families, most of whom were fishermen. The larger Guadalupe directly to the north was simply known as *Lupe* by the locals. This off-path tourist destination consisted of a small but growing population of shopkeepers and restaurant workers, traditional architecture with sparse new, gaudy American-style development thrown in.

Tommy watched the few lights being switched on in the small fishing village that hugged the long crescent shaped bay's glassy waters. A mile or so north of the settlement more lights shone out from the little town itself. In the fading twilight the boy could see the outline of a dozen or so *pangas*, a word for the boats whose name translates to hatchet, since their upswept bow causes them to easily cut through rough seas. These boats, which are favored by everyone from fishermen to pirates in Mexican waters are outboard powered, eighteen feet long and painted pale blue. These particular *pangas* were resting from the long day and pulled up onto the damp, warm sand for the night while seagulls dove for the guts of the fish that had earlier lined their hulls. His only disappointment was that the bay's deep curve let in no surf except for the tiny shore break that thumped hard against clean sand. His heart lifted again at the realization that not far from here would be unexplored waves for the taking.

The loss of the muffler made sleep and conversation impossible and Jose drove faster, partially to avoid getting stuck again, but mostly in anticipation of seeing his little family. When he was still a quarter mile off, two large mutts came bounding toward the rusty old Chevrolet Apache. "Hello George Bush," Jose shouted, laughing to see the larger of the two dogs, a sad-eyed Labrador mix that had clumsily outrun the tall, thin, spotted female, Little Sarah, until it was outrun by two other dogs that were wild and had no names. The dogs charged up to the truck, wagging tails to greet them. Pepe jumped from Tommy's arms, clear out of the truck, taking a tumble in the soft sand shoulder, somersaulting before finding his feet and trying to keep up with the other, bigger dogs by running hard, yelping, wagging and competing to see who could get closest to the tires. Three children came running, not far behind the dogs. The two boys had given Lupita, the bright-faced young girl of about twelve a head start. Behind her was Baby Jose, a pudgy boy of about ten who laughed hard as he ran, smiling and waving to see Tommy, who waved back at him. The oldest boy, who was around Tommy's own age, ran behind the others before he broke away to outrun them. Getting to the truck first, he now outraced even the dogs. He had the serious appearance of a boxer or a big-wave surfer. His name was Santillo, but everyone called him Max. Max was shoeless and shirtless in faded jeans, his wide chest heaving as he ran with the long, smooth stride of a marathon winner.

When Jose slowed the truck to a crawl, Max, then the other children jumped onto the running boards as the dogs took turns snapping at the tires. Max glared at Tommy, not sure what to make of the *gringo* kid invading his family. Jose's wife Carmen stood in the distance like some 1950s movie poster against the clapboard shack, silhouetted by moonlight and waiting silently for her man on the wooden porch to see what surprises he had brought home from the U.S. this time.

Behold

# Chapter 5

# ENDLESS SURF TRIP

*Just as no two waves are identical, so it is with surf trips. The best ones are not planned and narrowly avoid disaster. Being held at gunpoint by bandits, run into a narrow ditch by an eighteen-wheeler, sitting in limbo with a blown engine, starving and penniless in a land where you don't know anyone and don't understand the language—these are all good ingredients for a great surf trip. In truth it really isn't about the surf at all, but the unknown reality that unfolds as the world you once knew spins out of control and you hang on by your fingernails, hoping to survive the new one.*

This surf trip began unlike any Tommy or anyone else had ever experienced. It was either going to be heaven or hell, and there was no end to it in sight. As they arrived at the shack Tommy noticed a pair of battered surfboards leaning against the wall of the house, along with a stack of half a dozen or so rusted lobster traps. The home itself was sprawling and sturdily made from a variety of cast off materials: broken cement blocks, weathered timbers, a garage door and the laminated wooden deck of an old sailboat were all evident in the construction. The fireplace was made entirely from smooth beach stones. Nine or ten skinny chickens roamed freely just beyond the structure. There was also a goat tied to a stake that Tommy would later realize was used for milking. Beyond this house was desert, interrupted by a smattering of small houses, the town and burnt out cinder cones, those remnants of small volcanic eruptions, in all directions but west, where the Pacific lay silently, true to its name.

Jose parked on the driveway, which was nothing but a patch of beach stones sunken into sand. Starting with Lupita, the children greeted him one at a time before piling onto him all at once, hugging and kissing. Not used to such affection among families, Tommy turned away. As Jose walked into the house, Tommy noticed that he had a severe limp. He had no way of knowing that this was the result of an old wound from a mako shark he once caught. When Jose attempted to release the shark, it turned and ripped into his calf, digesting a large hunk of flesh as it swam away. Still, Jose bore the shark no malice and when his leg hurt, as it often did, he would rub it, smile and say, "The shark was only being a shark."

The house mainly consisted of one big room where the kitchen and living room combined, surrounded by doors for the two bedrooms and the one bathroom. Jose was like a Mexican Santa Clause as he magically reached into his jacket pockets and pulled out small items for the children: painted hairclips for Lupita that she immediately put into her jet-black hair, a book on fishing for Baby Jose and a heavy leather jump rope for Max. As the children examined their treasures, Jose held Carmen for a long time. She was small in stature but sturdily built with a hint of ancient Mayan beauty that had not faded through her years of desperately hard work. Her skin was deeply creased and her once raven black hair was now streaked grey. Jose took a pair of crystal candlesticks, green candles and a new tablecloth from the gunnysack he had carried from the truck. After placing the gifts on the long wooden dinning room table, Carmen kissed her husband before a minor skirmish erupted between them about when dinner would be ready. Realizing that such tension always boils over after time away, the couple paused and broke into laughter, holding each other again before Jose introduced Tommy to everyone. With the greetings over, Tommy looked around and noticed there was no TV in sight. He would soon realize that nobody in the family owned a computer or a cell phone.

Each member of the Santiago family spoke good English, taught to the children at the apostolic school in town before being passed on to their parents. They were all glad for the visitor, except for Max who refused to acknowledge him. After a dinner of tortillas, beans and some lean chicken, Tommy found his way to the old couch where, without removing his clothes, he passed out for the night beneath the thin woven blanket Carmen draped over him. The next thing he knew he heard Max and Jose speaking softly while listening to a battery-operated weather radio. From the window he observed the infinite star field punctuating the black sky.

Father and son got into the truck, taking the short ride to the bay where the *panga* waited. Tommy, still in his clothes from the day before, quickly recalled the events leading him here and tried to clear his mind of them. Without shoes, he ran through the sand after the truck whose dust could be seen for a quarter mile. The Pacific was immaculately groomed by a stiff offshore wind, and sparsely lined with shells and fish skeletons being picked over by hundreds of seagulls. Despite its raw beauty, the place smelled of dried fish and diesel fuel. Silently, Jose placed the stout fishing rods into their holders as Tommy arrived just in time to help Max push the boat from the damp sand into water deep enough for the prop to clear the bottom.

After reaching sufficient depth Max jumped aboard, shoving Tommy back into the water when he attempted to join them. In the perfect English which everyone in the Santiago family possessed, except Jose who mixed up many words and could not shake his Mexican accent, Max shouted, "Go with the women *gringo*."

The dawn glowed pink as Tommy sauntered toward the house, turning occasionally to observe the powerful, minimal strokes of Jose, who smoothly rowed the boat into the current that would do most of the work, controlling the boat like a fine artist does a brush on a canvas. Next, it was Max's turn as he took deep, even strokes in the shallow water as tiny baitfish jumped in schools of thousands all around them, some falling into the *panga*, where Jose caught them by hand and placed them into the bait tank for later. They soon found depth enough for Jose to break the silence of the morning by pulling the chord to start the faithful Mercury engine that he had torn down and rebuilt countless times. The Mercury would again carry them out twenty miles, to the bank where the yellowtail broke the surface for as far as you could see. By the time Max and Jose were underway, the other fishermen had arrived in pairs, repeating the same ritual as the Santiago men had until six other boats were following Jose and Max out to sea. Tommy watched as the sun began its daily arc, clearing the hills to the east and painting the scattered clouds scarlet to signal a coming storm.

Back in the house, the boy observed the family coming to life. Lupita, still in flannel pajamas, sat so close to Tommy she was nearly on his lap as he joined the family in a meal of eggs, beans and tortillas called *huevos rancheros*. Carmen prided herself on the special sauce she made, and the hand-rolled tortillas she had prepared the previous evening. After strong coffee for Tommy and Carmen and raw goat's milk for the children, Tommy helped clean up, contemplating how he would tangle with the kid Max, before long.

With the work done the boy gathered his wetsuit and surfboard, to wander south, in search of surf. He had only walked a quarter mile past the bay, along the jagged coast when he noticed what looked to be whitewater wrapping into a small bay. He walked and ran the next half-mile of beach rock and soft sand, stubbing his toes on the cobbles that lined the point.

The waves proved only shoulder high, but powerful and he surfed them alone—like the wave-riding genius he was, carving big white fans on gun barrel grey faces—tearing into each section with world-class skill that was fueled by anger, twice pulling into the inside bowl before it slammed shut. He rode for nearly four hours with no other surfers in sight. With little warning the storm hit, turning the previously well-groomed ocean into a mess of blinding foam and disorganized white-capped waves. On his last wave, he picked up a small cut on his foot when it collided with a slick barnacle-encrusted rock near shore.

He made his way back toward the boat launch along the packed clay road that the rain had turned slick as ice. Tommy fell after every few steps, contemplating the waves he had ridden, wondering about their potential on a bigger swell. When he again came to the curvature of beach that defined the bay he saw the small boat returning, plowing through two-foot high chop, burying the bow in the trough of each wave before shooting back up, repeating the process again and again. Steadily making its way home, the boat rode lower in the water than it had at daybreak, indicated a good catch.

Once on shore Tommy helped unload the twenty-some yellowtail, all over twenty pounds with two topping out around thirty. Also in the hull, still thrashing were two white sea bass, the larger of them measuring from the ground to a man's chin. Four or five halibut whose length were the width of a kitchen table and a thresher shark that ran more than half the length of the eighteen-foot *panga* were also on board. It was their best day all season. The catch once filleted would bring a good price in town–enough to keep the family in essentials for a few months.

Realizing he was unneeded by the fishermen, Tommy continued walking toward the house in the rain while Max and Jose loaded the fish onto the tailgate of the truck. They filleted them effortlessly with a few flicks of the wrist without wasting any of the precious meat and throwing the remains back into the shallows for the crabs and seagulls that sometimes intercepted them in flight, or fought over them in the water. Once filleted, the steaks were wrapped in butcher paper and placed in one of three large ice chests. They worked without speaking until Jose sliced his finger with his razor-sharp filet knife and shouted *cathrone*, a curse word he rarely used and never said in front of the younger children. After cursing, Jose lifted the crucifix around his neck to his lips and kissed it; something he did each time he said that or other bad words. He took the bandanna from his neck and wrapped his finger in it before returning to work in the now consistently hard rain.

Meanwhile Tommy had arrived at the house, finding Carmen inside with the kids that had returned from school early since the school building could easily flood in such conditions. The children sat quietly doing homework while their mother mended clothes on her old foot-propelled sewing machine. The big lab, George Bush was asleep on the rocker Jose had recently carved from a single piece of wood as the three other dogs huddled near the warm woodstove, fortifying one another against the storm outside in the leaky wooden house. Occasionally Lupita would glance shyly from her schoolbooks at Tommy, who sat on a thick rug near the fire, hoping for something to occupy himself. Finally Lupita called out, "Your real name is Tomás not Tommy. It's like Santo Tomás, a town nearby." Tommy forced a smile and nodded as the little girl shuffled over, head down and sat on the rug, near him. "Tomás, where are your parents?" asked the little girl.

Tommy hesitated as Max and Jose walked in. The hard rain had caused them to suspend their work until the next day. They were drenched in a mixture of rainwater and fish blood, tired and talking happily of the good catch. Carmen took their boots and coats, returning with clean dry towels, socks, pants and shirts that they went to their rooms to change into before standing on the wooden floor near the fire. Without hesitation or pity, she brought alcohol and gauze bandages for Jose's injured finger and tended to the wound silently while everyone else settled in. Max had figured correctly that the visitor was in the process of answering the question everyone was curious about. Having stalled for a while it was asked again, this time by Max. "So, where are your parents, *gringo?*"

"My mother and father are arriving on a cruise ship from San Diego to Ensenada. I will meet them later this week," said Tommy, using an excuse he had composed only that moment. Everyone realized there were great holes in this story.

Jose, who knew for sure it was a lie, came to Tommy's rescue, saying, "I picked this boy up in Ensenada when he could not find no room at the hotel." Everyone knew Jose was as honest as a man could be, but Max didn't believe a word of it. Only Lupita believed Tommy's story completely.

"How long will you stay with us?" asked Carmen.

"Just a few days," answered Tommy.

Everyone returned to work or rest as the little girl settled into telling Tommy about her school, her friends and how to pronounce words correctly, in Spanish. After her mother called the girl back to her schoolwork, Max approached Tommy and whispered, "Your parents are on vacation in Ensenada?" When Tommy refused to answer, Max continued, "We don't like *gringo* surfers down here. I want you to leave before your parents return from vacation." Tommy rose from the floor to meet his opponent. Not wanting to disturb the rest of the family, however, he opened his clenched fist as Max palmed the boy's shoulder and walked away.

Max retreated to a corner of the house where he scoured a fishing magazine in the dim light, glancing up to scowl menacingly at Tommy every so often. Raining or not, Tommy decided to make his escape early the next morning and head further south.

Behold

$$=============\ Chapter\ 6\ =============$$

# GUADALUPE

*Any day in Baja can offer a surfer things now extinct in Southern California–perfect six-foot lines peeling into an azure bay shared by nobody but the surfers you came with, and fishermen selling lobster tacos for a buck or two. Any day can bring ruler-edged point surf, a fish the size of a refrigerator, or a desert grave courtesy of bandits or Federales.*

Tommy was up well before the sun the next morning, carrying his few belongings plus the pocketknife he lifted from the kitchen counter. When he opened the door, however, he was met with a downpour so violent that water surrounded the little house like a castle moat. He quickly shut the door on the flashflood. All roads were knee-deep in water, and there would be no way in or out of Santa Guadalupe for at least a week. He placed the knife back where he found it and watched the family come to life. Carmen made hot coffee, chocolate and breakfast, which everyone ate together before they helped wash up, and the children began homework. Jose, who was the only family member not at breakfast, took the rare opportunity to sleep in. The storm left the two wild animals, Max and Tommy, in the same cage. Noting there was no wind accompanying this storm and realizing that a solid swell was hitting from the south, Max decided he would take the *panga* to the point. He distrusted Tommy, but needed someone to help launch the boat, so reluctantly motioned for the *gringo* to join him. Max pulled on his old wetsuit that had been patched with duct tape and fishing line as Tommy did the same with his newer wetsuit. Once outside, Max retrieved the smaller of the two boards he had found drifting in the current offshore, from the side of the house. Tommy took his board from the bed of Jose's truck. The truck could not negotiate the roads on days like this, so they walked and slid through the mud in their wetsuits, boards under their arms.

On the way to the launch, Max thrust the pointy nose of his board into Tommy's ribs. Tommy dropped his board in the mud, wrenched Max's board from his grip and threw it violently onto the ground. Immediately, Max was on him, punching him in the face, and opening up his lip. Tommy's punches missed each time as Max, who was training to be a boxer, easily slipped each one of them. Max soon had Tommy on the ground, pushing his head into the mud while showering him with hard punches. While Tommy was defenseless, Max realized that the *gringo* would not quit until he was dead. He hoped to hurt the boy, not kill him, and so Max let him up, but not before slapping him across the face, more as an insult than to inflict pain. When Tommy finally connected, Max retaliated with a final punch that again dropped his opponent into the mud. Without hesitation or apology, they continued moving on toward the surf.

Once at the launch the ocean was a sheet of silver glass marred only by hard rain. The big swells could be seen rolling past the bay, far out at sea. Neither of the boys talked as they loaded their boards and freed the boat from the sand. Max pulled the rope to start the engine, and they settled into the twenty-minute ride, finding the point a surfer's dream, solid six to eight feet, turquoise blue pock marked by the now fading raindrops; the lined-up waves framed in white under light offshore winds, long hollow sections, deep hard breaking caverns peeling over smooth cobblestone and a sandy beach fronted by tall sandstone cliffs. Nobody was out, and nobody was coming. Max dropped anchor and jumped over the side without even looking at the surf, leaving Tommy alone in the boat to watch the dreamscape unfold before him. He could barely imagine empty surf of this caliber in the past, but now, seeing it, he did not react by charging into it. Instead he sat, his gut churning as visions of the Mexican prison he would probably rot in poisoned his thoughts.

Max, who rode a delaminated 5'6" Rusty squash tail, took off late on the first wave of the set, a wave that was well overhead, set his rail and pulled into a solid barrel before exiting the tube and moving into a series of decent cutbacks. Like the place he came from, Max was not flashy but functional, blending smoothly into each section the way a pelican glides over the air current ahead of a wave.

His morbid meditations complete, Tommy jumped overboard onto the 6'10" pintail, a board made for bigger waves than those he was about to ride. He paddled out to where Max, who already had ridden three waves, sat with his back facing him, the only other surfer for miles. A set wave rose in the kelp outside, backed off and steepened as Max dropped in, did a deep turn and disappeared beneath the curtain for a long tube ride. The next wave was Tommy's, and while he sat deep in the tube, racing in and out of hollow sections, the big board did not allow him the freedom of movement he would have enjoyed on smaller equipment. Max nodded approval when Tommy exited an inside tube and pulled out next to him.

*Nobody was out and nobody was coming.*

The two paddled out in silence. As the tide dropped and the rain subsided it left the sky dotted with puffy white pillows on cobalt

35

blue laid upon the point's turquoise. Some of the best waves on the West Coast belonged exclusively to them, and they could no longer keep from hooting as each wave peeled off like a hand-drawn miracle.

After three hours, Tommy felt comfortable enough to ask Max to trade boards. Without a word, Max undid his brittle leash and pushed the 5'6" to Tommy in trade for the bigger board. Max's conservative surfing style actually suited the longer board, finding it fast through sections, while Tommy held back on the small board at first, letting a long section fold in front him before breaking free of the whitewater and clearing the section with a distant floater before dropping back in and launching into a three foot aerial, which sent him flying over the wave, and landed him on the flats. As the next section threatened to break in front of him, he pumped a half turn and did another long floater that landed him in just the right spot, back on the face, where he threw the board into a series of vertical snaps. Max, who had only seen moves like that in the few surf magazines he owned, watched, paddled over to Tommy, and splashed him playfully. Tommy was unsure if Max's gesture was friendly or a veiled threat. He looked up tensely, ready to strike if need be, before Max laughed and Tommy laughed nervously. After another hour, the wind hit. At first it was a puff, then it blew with greater power, side shore, from the south causing the previously perfect waves to crumble into piles of disorganized mush.

Before staring the motor, Max pulled anchor, set a drift line and let the *panga* float toward shore before pulling up a fifteen-pound halibut in less than ten minutes. After gaffing the fish and wrestling it onboard, he yanked the chord to start the motor and they were off, fighting chop all the way home as Max twisted the throttle and made record time back to the safety of the bay.

During the short boat ride, Max was first to speak. "I thought you were a kook," he said. "But I like the way you tube ride, dragging your hand to stay in the barrel. You'll have to teach me that." Tommy did not reply, but touched his still swollen lip in remembrance of the punch he would someday repay.

In mere hours the old world vanished, and Tommy decided to live in the new one–in Santa Guadalupe he would surf and learn the ways of a fisherman. He was not aware that an invisible net had been cast, something that would hold him and teach him more than he ever imagined. He would learn about the give and take of the tide and the give and take of a family as they struggled as one to make a life for themselves in an environment that would challenge a scorpion. In that moment, Tomás and Max were unaware of anything but the feeling brought on by the good surf they had ridden, not realizing they were forging unbreakable bonds for a lifetime as they were born again in some unexplainable way, as brothers. This day would be the first of many like it for the pair. While Max was being led into the world of a serious wave rider, the newly christened Tomás was being immersed in a world governed by forces greater than himself—learning of reefs and fish migrations, each day fuller than the next for him, an accumulation of sunrises and sunsets, huge fish pulled from great depths, bigger ones seen but not landed and waves that left you drifting off to sleep where you dreamed the dreams of kings.

The next three years passed as if they were as many weeks for Tomás and the Santiago family. Life was measured by fishing seasons, birthdays, religious holidays and the occasional *Quinceañera* to celebrate a girl's 15th birthday and her coming into womanhood. On one such occasion there had been a big party for Lupita who had gone from a cute little girl to a beautiful young woman with her mother's charm and habit of being able to listen patiently to any problem, along with the wisdom to solve many of them.

Everything remained the same except that Jose Senior's calf muscle, which had never completely healed after the shark swallowed much of it whole, began to bother him greatly. With no money for surgery he kept fishing in spite of the pain. Finally, unable to continue, he managed the fishing operation from shore, making necessary repairs to the *panga* and doing all the cash transactions, including taking the catch into town and, twice a month, to the Ensenada Harbor where he received a better price than he could in Guadalupe.

Max and Tomás skippered the little boat, which was used less to transport them to surf and more to take them into deep water where they hauled out fish, including some massive tuna, some so big they threatened to capsize the boat. From March through October, which is lobster season, they would use the lobster traps they built from scrap wire by hand. They would bait them with fish heads, attach the traps to woven nylon lines tied to plastic buoys and set them in twenty feet of water on the inside reef. When they pulled the trap the next morning they usually found a dozen or so big lobsters ready to be sold live at the market in Puerto Nuevo to the north.

Each May they followed the halibut spawn, drifting in shallow water for five or six big fish at a time, snagging dozens of the flat fish that have no eyes on the bottom and two eyes on top, and according to Jose were "half blind, like many people I have known." Halibut are ambush hunters that camouflage themselves, blending into the sandy patches, waiting to gulp down anchovies and sardines. What they lack in looks, they make up for in taste, so Pacific Halibut is a prize whose filets can weigh up to ten pounds each, and bring top dollar. They provided a treat to the Santiago family, who ate every part of the fish with gratitude to God and shared the catch with neighbors all quick to find their door whenever the season arrived.

By the fall of 2008 the catch had been steadily declining. One evening at dinner Max pounded his fist onto the kitchen table, shouting, "It's those damn purse seiners that take everything, netting entire schools of migrating tuna that they fatten in pens like pigs. To make matters worse the tuna have to eat, so all the baitfish are netted, stealing the food supply from all other fish." Many Mexican fishermen feared they would soon be out of work and a worthy family industry that had lasted hundreds of years would be wiped out in a single decade. The idea of working in town in the tourist industry or crossing the border to find work in the U.S. digging ditches to help build houses for single yuppie couples with no kids but big enough for ten families, angered Max. "These are the same ones ruining everything," he said. "The only help I will give them is to dig their graves. Some day I will take the boat to Ensenada, dive down, cut the cages open and free all the tuna." Before the words ever left his mouth he realized this was a hopeless dream. Like the working poor around the world, Max often struggled with anger. His struggle was not with hate, as some might assume, but with too much love–he loved life in Guadalupe so dearly he could not bear to see it disappear beneath the wheel of progress. When, on occasion, his anger boiled over, he knew exactly how to vent it.

Behold

# Chapter 7

# THE FIGHTER

*In traditional Mexican families, the father is the head of the household. He has the final say in allowing a couple to date and at the time of a wedding proposal to officially approve his daughter to marry and be given in marriage.*

Margarita Sanchez lived in Guadalupe with her parents and two brothers. The family owned the Guadalupe Hotel, a weatherworn, two-story twelve-room destination in town with an ocean view. This brought the Sanchez family in closer touch with U.S. customs than most who lived in rural Baja. She was a Catholic girl educated for a time at the Episcopal Bishop's School in La Jolla, California. Max, on the other hand, was a born and bred fisherman with practical knowledge who rarely left Guadalupe and had barely finished ninth grade. While he could read the sea and sky better than most anyone, he had learned little from books, and nothing of the ways of what is often called "polite company." As such some well-educated people, whose neckties could choke off true knowledge, often considered him ignorant. He was well mannered when need be, but knowing which fork to use at dinner, or what wine went with what dish was useless in his eyes. Margarita, who had been raised in such nonsense, quit caring about the superficial world after falling in love with Max. Actually she had loved him since they were young children playing Marco Polo, where they each let the other catch them as they blindly moved about the hotel pool. By age fourteen they were going steady. Now, four years later Max approached Pablo Sanchez, Margarita's father, to request his daughter's hand in marriage, a formal request known as *pedir*. After some consideration on Pablo's part, and Margarita teaching Max about things like salad forks and linen napkins, Pablo Sanchez agreed to the marriage. That night Max proposed directly to

Margarita under the stars offering her the entire heavens rather than a mere gem to seal their love. She quite naturally said yes.

On the first Saturday of each month Max and Tomás, who were both now eighteen-years-old, drove Jose's 1974 Chevy pickup to Ensenada. By now the truck had been rebuilt a hundred times and Tomás was nearly as good at fixing it as were Max and Jose. The trips to town were not luxury cruises for the brothers, but a chance to sell fish and for Max to earn some real money boxing as a semi pro.

Many days found them on the side of the dusty road to Guadalupe digging out Mercedes and BMW's from the soft sand and paid twenty bucks for their efforts. This day they didn't stop for the stranded tourists they saw—they were on their way to a big fight. So far Max had had eleven fights, lost two and won the rest, six by knockout.

While none of the matches were easy, the coming one would be among the most difficult tests of his life. Max, who was 5'10" and 165 pounds, was fighting for the title in the middleweight division, and the man he was facing was the regional champion and so brutal in the ring he had earned the name *El Asesino,* The Assassin.

Max had used Tomás as a sparring partner, roping off a ring in the dirt adjacent to the house. Working in the soft sand aided Max in building his calf muscles and endurance. Max's punches fell like rain on Tomás who usually missed when trying to hit back. When he finally did connect however, he sent Max onto the sand, and he knew and Max knew this was for the punch he had taken years earlier. Max did not retaliate. In fact, from then on he took it easy on Tomás and concentrated strictly on conditioning–running for miles in the soft sand while carrying heavy boulders, doing 500 pushups a day, 1,000 sit-ups and 100 pull-ups on the lone scrub oak tree in front of the house. Whenever they went fishing, Max would pull the *panga* the quarter mile from the house to the shore as Tomás shouted encouragement to him while jogging alongside.

While the rest of the family pleaded to attend the fight, Max felt they would be a distraction and decided to have only the stoical

Tomás, his corner man, for company. The ride to Ensenada had been somber; in the locker room, Tomás silently wrapped Max's hands with the white gauze wraps used by Mexican fighters. Before removing his T-shirt and having Tomás lace up his gloves, Max crossed himself and kissed the cross he wore, pulling it from his neck and handing it to Tomás who kissed it and placed it in his own pants' pocket. The little arena was dark and smelled of beer, disinfectant and cigarettes. A tattered mat held together with duct tape carpeted

the plywood floor of the ring. Still, it seemed the entire male population of Ensenada was there to see the fight, which had been advertised on the radio and on posters from Tijuana to Ensenada.

While Max's opponent was as tough as they came, he was not very smart and within six rounds Max had tricked him into punching himself out. Max covered himself with his arms near the ropes as *El Asesino* threw his best shots. "Rope-a-dope" the great Ali had named it. His cruel opponent punched so hard that at times Max felt his only defense, his arms, were ready to break. Little by little the shots began losing their sting. The man was tiring. When Max looked up to see the champ breathing through his mouth, he knew his time had come. Max rested on the ropes, playing dead a little longer before bouncing to life off the ropes and letting go with a combination of punches that fell like a dozen hammers, followed by a single jackhammer hook that sent the champ to the canvas. At the count of four he staggered to his feet but was quickly knocked down again. After the champion was counted out, Max's bruised and swollen arm was raised in victory. He then walked over to congratulate his fallen opponent, collect his big belt and the 525-dollar purse. Max cashed the check in a liquor store in town, gave Tomás a hundred-dollar bill, and recklessly stuffed his pockets with the remaining bills before driving straight to Hussong's Cantina with Tomás to celebrate with tequila and beer.

As Tomás walked into the cantina, he heard the familiar hissing of a lit M-80, a quarter stick of dynamite, and turned to see it burning in Max's hand. Out in front of the cantina, two *Federales* sat, waiting in their car. Tomás, who was wary of the cops, fell in with the crowd and pushed his way inside. Max lobbed the little bomb into the back seat of the *Federales'* car and, *boom,* the car's back windows were shattered as guns were instantly drawn and the furious *Federales* were locked and loaded on the street as Max followed Tomás and lost himself in the crowd waiting at the entrance. Finding nobody to blame, the *Federales* grabbed a couple of local skateboarders, cuffed them, put them into the back seat of the car, slapped them around, warned them and let them go.

Max's face was covered with cuts, welts, bumps and bruises from the fight, but he was happy and in such a mood to celebrate that he arrogantly wore his prize belt into Hussong's before removing it and slapping it onto the bar. Tomás' face darkened, the sick stench of alcohol reminding him that this same liquid had destroyed his father. Max, who still knew nothing of this, pestered Tomás to have a drink with him. When Tomás continued to refuse, Max pushed him off his barstool onto the floor. Tomás knew not to react, but simply pulled himself up again and waited patiently for Max to get drunk.

The drunker Max became the louder he shouted, screaming out that he was the toughest man in the world and would give a hundred dollars to anyone who could take his belt from him. The first man to come forward was fallen by a quick right cross. So was the second. Nobody tested Max again until a new crew arrived.

Within an hour, Hussong's was packed with locals and weekend college kids from across the border. Most of the kids from up north were respectful, and some, like the young missionaries, even volunteered to work in the local orphanage on weekends. Then there were the loud momma's boys in tight T-shirts, sporting random tattoos that usually had no connection to anything important. Just like them, their shiny new four-wheelers had never been challenged in rough terrain.

Max again shouted a challenge which three frat boys took up. After beating him to the ground, they took the belt and all of Max's cash and left him on the floor. As the bar erupted in violence and Max's friends beat and then chased the invaders from the bar, Tomás ran and hid in the truck.

Tomás had run at the first sign of trouble, not because he was a coward, but because he knew that any attention from the *Federales* would lead to a prison cell. More than an hour later, Max staggered to the truck to find Tomás slumped low in the driver's seat. Seemingly not overly worried at his loss or his beating, Max jabbed at his brother playfully and said, "It's okay that *mi hermano* is a chicken.

You drive and I'll fight." With that Max kissed Tomás on the cheek, threw him his keys and fell in and out of consciousness in the passenger's seat while his brother drove home through the back streets in order to avoid the *Federales*.

As Tomás drove cautiously home, the drunken Max would occasionally come to and shout out the window at the black sky that he was going back to shoot the bandits who had robbed him. It was an empty threat he could never accomplish since he was a normally sober, practical kid who had never owned or even fired a gun. Once home, Tomás helped his brother from the truck to the front room. But they were not celebrating and singing as drunken fools do in "B" movies. As the full weight of his foolishness fell upon him, Max sat and pounded the table hard before laying his head there and weeping until he fell asleep in the chair. How could he tell his family and especially Margarita that he had defeated his opponent and was beaten by his own pride? Tomás removed his brother's shoes, covered him with a blanket and watched him fall into a deep sleep.

It took two weeks before the shouting and threats to break off the marriage died down from Margarita. Then, when all was forgiven, the wedding was planned for Saturday, November 5, 2008 at Our Lady of Guadalupe Church in Ensenada. The wedding was pretty and quiet, the sober Max barely audible when repeating his vows. After quitting alcohol for the most part and boxing entirely, Max and Margarita lived harmoniously in the little house Max and Tomás built for them next door to the Santiago family. The place was just big enough for them and the arrival of Max and Margarita's first child, a son who was forever called "Lil Jose." In time they would expand the little house to accommodate all the children they and the entire Santiago family joyfully anticipated.

The next two years passed without incident, everyone happy and healthy and waiting for the fish to return, which they never did in great numbers. Max and Tomás–less often Jose–ran the boat further and further out to sea, to a secret reef only they knew, making a decent living on the fish they caught. Lobsters, those tasty cockroaches of the sea, thrived because of the increasing filth pumped into the ocean. The lobsters compensated for the bad years of fishing, and while they never got rich, there was enough for a new motor and some surfboard materials from the States that Tomás was familiar enough with to make boards for himself and his brother.

Lupita, meanwhile, had become the talk of the little town—hair of black silk and obsidian eyes that hid her gaze that was fixed mainly on her adopted brother. She wondered if anyone could detect the sound of her beating heart that raced each time the young man came near. Also unseen was the reason for the depth of the girl's beauty that came from her hours of lonely prayer that she made mostly for her immediate family and increasingly for her secret love, Tomás.

Jose senior was less active than before and now wanted to pass on his knowledge to his children. He had done a good job of this with the fishing trade, but he had also been a part-time mariachi in his youth, and one of the few things he insisted everyone in his family do was learn to play a musical instrument. Even Tomás learned guitar and the old Mexican songs that were often played in the Santiago house. There were no more births, no deaths or tragedies in the home for a long time and life fell into that peaceful rhythm that never lasts more than a few seasons for even the most blessed among us. Votive candles in the church and at home were lit in gratitude, and as a hedge against the devil that knocks at the doors of even the best Mexican families. These should have been times of great joy for the entire family. And they were, except for Tomás, who worked hard and was never disobedient in any way, but generally remained distant from everyone. At those times when darkness fell over the face of the boy, he would be unreachable for days. His unsettled look perfectly mirrored the storm that had yet to begin brewing in the Gulf of Alaska and would soon come down the coast, threatening everything in its way.

Behold

# Chapter 8

# MEXICAN CHRISTMAS

*Christmas season in a small Mexican village is a fine thing to be-hold. The village is calm and bright with decorations and images of the Nativity displayed on the streets and in homes. Homemade tamales are in every home with an abundance of seafood on the coast and carne asada favored inland. Baskets are filled with great varieties of delicious fruit and Mexican bread called pan. The families are at rest from their hard lives and functional items or small handmade art pieces are exchanged with the giver's entire heart attached to them.*

Tomás had a sturdy fishing knife for Max, a solid oak cane with a sil-ver-plated handle for Jose and colorful hair clips for Carmen, Lupita and Margarita. He made a wooden cross to be hung over the crib of Lil Jose and gave an English Grammar book to Baby Jose.

The entire town of Santa Guadalupe lit up for a Christmas that included three days of feasting on white sea bass and yellowtail. The Santiago home itself was decorated with a living Manzanita Tree for a Christmas tree that they had dug up inland. There were many little wrapped presents beneath it, including gifts for anyone that came to the door days before the holiday. The onyx manger scene was prominently displayed, and handmade paper stars decorated every room in the house. Candies and pan were out for anyone that wanted them. Everyone gained a few pounds awaiting the arrival of the Christ child.

It had been five years since Tommy Stern, now known to everyone in the little settlement as Tomás Santiago, had moved to Santa Guadalupe. His long apprenticeship as a fisherman was complete and he could operate the boat alone, tear down and rebuild the engine, tie and untie any knot, bait hooks with just the right fish, and fillet a fish with a couple clean slices of the blade. Tomás loved his work, and slowly, cautiously found the ability to love the Santiago family, who were the closest thing to a real family he had known since childhood. Jose had become like a father to him, teaching him the vast skills needed to fish this coast. Carmen was the loving mother he had not known since he was an infant, touching his hair with matronly love from time to time, encouraging him in his work and making sure he was always fed. Max was his brother and his best friend.

Lupita, who was now seventeen-years-old, had been attracted to Tomás since the first day they met. And while Tomás had, over time, also become attracted to Lupita, he never admitted it, even to himself. He merely looked out for the young girl as one would a little sister. But Lupita made no secret to herself of her feelings for the boy who had been guided to manhood by her father's firm hand. Her childhood crush had turned to love and by now it burned hot. But she and Tomás never acted on or spoke of such things.

On her first date, Tomás drove with Lupita in the family truck, while each heart ached for the other. Tomás accompanied the girl to the movies where he sat next the young boy, discouraging him when he tried putting his arm around his little sister.

Baby Jose, who was now simply called Jose, was almost a grown man himself and away from home a lot, since he had chosen to work as a teacher's aid in Guadalupe until he graduated high school and earned enough money to go to college and receive a credential to teach English. As for Jose Senior, the shark wound ached constantly now. He mostly worked from home near Carmen, whose saintliness was reflected in her hair that was worn like a silver crown.

Max handled the fishing boat with Tomás; the two of them surfing a few hours a day or all day long whenever the waves were too big for them to fish the offshore reefs. Nobody who saw Tomás would ever guess he had once been an up and coming American surfer, a thief and a murderer who had arrived in the village as a scared boy half a decade earlier. His hair, which was always shaded by a straw hat, was cut short and had returned to its native dark brown, while any exposed skin had become dark and leathery. His hands had hardened from being cut and scared over by foolishly trying to hold the monofilament lines when a big fish ran for deep water. He spoke perfect Spanish in the style of country people. If anyone asked, which nobody ever did, his name was Tomás Santiago, he was born and raised in Santa Guadalupe and his occupation was that of fisherman. Nobody could remember anything different. But Tomás *did* remember things.

Behold

# Chapter 9

# THE WAVE

*Deep-water canyons can condense ocean swells and cause them to rise to many times their normal height. Offshore islands in Baja like Todos Santos come alive when big Aleutian storms produce massive swells along the West Coast of the U.S. While Todos has become famous for waves that often top twenty feet, there are waves on offshore islands so big and dangerous that surfers, fishermen and even ocean-going freighters avoid them.*

From the time he was a child, Tomás knew all there was to know about how swells were born in the violence of great storms. The waves arrived from the southwest in late summer before they hit the West Coast after being churned up by cyclones and then fanned out for thousands of miles. South facing beaches like Newport where Tomás had been born and raised took a direct hit from southwest swells. Direct south swells were birthed below Baja where hurricanes known as *Chubascos* created big waves that also pounded the West Coast in late summer, turning spots like Newport Point into miniature versions of Pipeline, and Trestles into a long and perfect point break. The winter swells, which formed the biggest, most powerful surf in this hemisphere originated in the Aleutian Island chain in the Gulf of Alaska. This is where Hawaii and the entire west coast from Alaska to Argentina got their biggest surf, much of it unloading on the way to hammer Mexico and its hidden points that produce corrugated lines of waves that could be ridden for minutes.

Once about every ten years or so an Aleutian swell broke off at just the right angle to bring some of the biggest surfable waves in the world within a boat ride of Tomás' adopted home. The fisherman wisely steered clear of such violence, using the valuable time off to make needed repairs to their *pangas* and other fishing equipment.

Jose, who was at the core of a group of old fisherman, had warned his sons about the big swell on its way. This was more than a once in a decade phenomena; it was a freak sent to punish the fishermen for their sins every century or so. "Bless me Father for I have sinned," Jose said in the confessional. As he made a good act of contrition the other fishermen stood in line to tell of all the bad they had done to cause the big storm. In reality, however, it probably had nothing to do with anyone's drunkenness, petty theft, infidelity or lying; it was a strong *El Nino*, a warming of water in the equatorial Pacific that sucked in the big rainstorms and brought massive waves with them.

Rain had been bearing down on Guadalupe for days as the Santiago family huddled close, praying for the poor in Tijuana, some who lived in the city dump, their skimpy shelters often washed away by rain less violent than this. There were also prayers for the rich in the U.S., especially those who cared for nothing but big empty houses, and never knew love like that which radiated through this little house.

As the rain cleared, the swell hit, keeping all the *pangas* anchored to the sand since it was far too dangerous to venture out past the bay's protection. Beyond anyone's vision twenty-foot seas had increased to forty-foot, with some waves approaching sixty. The storm had raged for days in the Aleutians, churning hundreds of miles of ocean into waves so big they could, as surf legend Buzzy Trent once said, only be "measured in increments of fear." These waves could clear out the shipping lanes of even the biggest craft and make the ocean fit for nothing but those creatures who called it home, most of whom would find shelter in the depths, when even the sun was obscured by massive walls of water.

Max was a good surfer by anyone's standards, fearless and a natural who would have been able to keep up with most in the States if he was not tied to work most days and could enjoy the endless summers often subsidized by U.S. families whose good intentions could keep their babies forever in diapers. Where Tomás had a great understanding of how waves broke, he knew little else until Jose and

Max taught him to read the ocean like a book by observing currents, wind direction and terns that hovered over bait balls.

There were decent waves less than a mile from the house and excellent ones at the point, a short boat ride away from the landing. In the surf Tomás was the master, a freak of nature that comes along rarely in a lifetime. He didn't merely ride a surfboard, he nearly made it articulate. Tomás blasted big airs and sat deep in the tube while Max continued riding with a more conservative style based around hard turns and cutbacks and the occasional tube ride. While the two surfed, they often set hoop nets on the reef, netting half a dozen large lobsters, which they brought home and boiled live in a pot before sharing the feast with family and neighbors. Sometimes they would dive overboard and come up with a lobster in each hand, or an eight or nine inch green abalone that they popped off the bottom with a screwdriver. They seemed unconcerned of any dangers, even from the big mako sharks, those fast, vicious predators that patrolled the area thirsty for anything containing blood.

Max was a great diver, rower, and all-around athlete in the ocean, something known respectfully in the surfing world as a "waterman." On one breath of air without a tank, he could dive seventy-five feet straight down. He had speared fish of over sixty pounds and when they swam for the bottom, fifty feet below, he dove down and cut them out of the kelp before swimming them back to the surface. He was as calm in the ocean as if he were himself a fish, never fighting currents and tides but moving with them. Over the years Max taught Tomás more about the rhythm of the sea than most surfers will ever understand. Like their father, Jose, Max and now Tomás had learned these things only because their lives depended on them.

When the swell arrived on Thursday, January 4th it was so big that even the bay was showing four-foot surf and the *pangas* had to be pulled up further onto the sand berm in order to keep them from being lost at sea. The wind blew favorably offshore, which is the only wind surfers like since it grooms waves smoothly rather than blowing them out. Not even Jose, who had fished here for over forty years, could remember such a swell. While the fishermen retreated to dry land and waited for the waves to subside, the big swells brought the boys to life early that morning to launch the *panga* and ride the point. They rode the glassy waters for two hours until the waves increased so much they began to close out the channel. On his last wave, Max noted that his brother had gone from a mere great surfer to a fine artist, playing with a wave as big as ever hit the California coast as if it were a three-foot shore break–dropping in on tiptoes, turning hard with sheets of water coming off the rail before pulling into a deep cavern, sitting in the tube for long seconds until the wave finally walled off and broke without exit in the channel.

Max and Tomás often spoke of the island that was sometimes visible from shore, eighteen miles away. It was not an island really, but nothing more than a little volcanic rock where some said the waves topped even those of the famed Mexican big-wave spot Killers on Isla Todos Santos. Max had seen perfect waves when fishing there with his father years earlier. From land it was a dot barely visible on the horizon. Yet, on that day, a faint white semicircle could be observed, even from shore. What looked small from shore were actually great plumes of whitewater blowing up around the island's edges.

On the previous night the boys had stripped all the wax from their biggest boards and re-waxed them in anticipation of this epic swell. With no place to buy surf wax, they used bars of paraffin that they heated in a pot on the stove and painted with an old paintbrush onto the decks of their boards. This is how surfers had waxed their boards until the sixties when the company, Surf Research, created custom surf wax.

When the brothers silently agreed to head to the island, Max turned the boat out toward sea from the point. They began moving into the face of the increasingly large swell, the eighteen foot *panga* soon dwarfed by waves nearly twice its height, the engine sputtering, prop spinning as they cleared the crest and then plunged down the back and fell hard into the trough with a slap, not certain that even the sturdy *panga* would hold each time it dropped from such a height. Once in the trough, they would become partially submerged before plowing up the face of the next wave, repeating the process hundreds of times until the island showed itself clearly and the swells decreased in the shadow of the little land mass. They had been at sea for two hours, and their gas was hovering at the halfway mark when the waves hitting the island's reef became clearly visible.

What they saw was terrifyingly beautiful—massive waves finding the depth of water to break on a reef far from land before exploding with perfect symmetry. What they could not see, however, was that the waves had traveled thousands of miles before being forced over a submerged mountain range into a narrow crevice that focused the swell and caused each wave to jack up to many times its original height, before encountering water shallow enough for all that energy to detonate on the reef. There was no way of telling how big the waves were now, but even the smallest of them were twenty feet, the sets topping thirty or more and breaking so hard they could hear and feel their deep rumblings even from where they sat in the boat, nearly two miles away.

They approached the island reverently and cautiously. Within half an hour they saw that the waves dwarfed even the gigantic lava boulders that lined the shore. This was no place for them in their tiny boat, no place for people without the safety of a big boat with a full crew, an emergency inflatable, safety vests, and the backup of a jet ski. Really, it was no place for anyone at all.

Fighting the impossibly powerful current, they dropped anchor, the boat rising beneath each massive swell and spinning in circles. They looked into the eye of a wave that was huge even by Hawaiian standards. These massive fluid mountains were something few people in the world wanted any part of, but something that drew and repulsed Tomás and Max with equal force. When draw won out over repulsion, they knew they had to go. Neither of them had a watch, but they estimated the biggest sets at about twenty minutes apart. With ragged wetsuits and crude handmade surfboards, they were severely underprepared for the challenge. As Tomás wondered at the wisdom of surfing this day, suddenly, without a word, Max threw himself overboard and began paddling the big-wave board Tomás had built for him in the shed three years earlier. The board, an eight-foot pintail, was made for big surf, but not this big. That and the 7'10" pintail Tomás had built for himself were far too small. These waves required equipment known as big-wave guns, sometimes called "elephant guns"–narrow spears in the nine-foot-plus range.

Big waves move with such speed that fast paddling is required just to catch them. Most everything in Tomás wanted to turn back, and although he knew his best effort wouldn't be enough, he nonetheless jumped in behind Max, whose only safety feature, his surf leash, was even older and more brittle than his own. It was certain that the first wave to break on either of them would send a board to shore, to be demolished on the rocks, something that could mean death. As they paddled, they saw the first wave of the set approach–defiant, afraid of nothing, able to demolish anything foolish enough to be in its path. Head down, they continued paddling toward the channel. The waves were even bigger than they had appeared from the boat, city blocks of water that stood up and hit the shallow reef like a ten-car pileup. Once they had cleared the first set of waves, they moved into position behind the island, looking up occasionally for telltale signs of churned up water, indicating the takeoff spot. They arrived in the takeoff area between sets and it was calm but deep in white foam as they tried to think about and not to think about the waves that were coming or the sharks they knew circled beneath them.

To take their minds off the impending disaster, they spoke about the future as it was guaranteed. The topic focused on what they would do during Christmas, although neither was certain they would live to see that morning. Minutes dragged by like hours until from the north a wall of water rose after smashing, unseen by them, into Killers at Todos Santos, where the magazines would later report record-sized surf. The first wave in the set was on them like a landslide, challenging them and their ridiculously tiny surfboards. It took a dozen strokes to climb over the top of it, each second threatening to snap them, to bury them, to leave nothing bigger than a fingernail of their once proud bodies. Nobody would ever know what happened as not a trace of them or of the fiberglass and foam surfboards would be found to tell the tale. Neither of them wanted this wave, and they let it roll beneath them and then watched and heard it break a hundred yards inside of them, throwing whitewater plumes fifty feet into the air, looking to see the great wave rocking and nearly capsizing the *panga*, which would have been the end of them, since they had no other way of getting back to shore.

The next six waves step laddered, each wave breaking bigger and further out until the last of them approached thirty feet. They narrowly cleared these mountain tops, dropping from a great height and slapping down on the backs of each wave so hard it seemed their boards would break in two before they somehow found the arm strength to paddle further out to sea to face the next one.

As the Himalayan skyline subsided for a moment, they looked in to see the island as a speck in the distance. Without a word it was decided that this day was simply beyond them, and they decided to make the hard paddle back against the current to the *panga*. They had made some headway when the next set arrived and without enough strength to paddle back out again, made the only decision left open to them. They, verbally this time, agreed to take the next wave in. The first wave was a solid fifteen feet, perfectly shaped and brushed clean by the increasing offshore wind. The takeoff was surprisingly easy and so drew Max into it. Once he had committed to the wave, however, it jumped another five feet in size, and went vertical while stretching out in a line that raced ahead for what seemed like miles. Max paddled down and was pulled back to the top several times before his board connected with the steep face, and he finally took the elevator drop; the spray from the offshore wind blinded his eyes while he lost his stomach on the air drop and instinctively, miraculously, stayed on the board and connected with the flat water at the bottom. He made just enough of a turn to get beyond the explosive power that chased him for a hundred yards, the board chattering on the face, the wave steepening up, boiling when it encountered shallow spots on the reef and taking him half a mile beyond the takeoff spot. If he had not been terrified he would have enjoyed the ride of his life on a wave that finally, gently, released him into water so deep it could have been an infinite hole in the ocean.

Max had survived the wave, but felt no relief as he contemplated the distance he had traveled, something that did nothing but increase his paddle back to the boat. His lungs ached, and his arms were rubber as he finally lifted himself into the *panga* and watched Tomás, a dot on the horizon, paddle up and over three increasingly large waves, any one of which might take him down forever if they broke on him. It required every bit of the tremendous knowledge and skill he possessed to out guess where the waves would land. As the first wave threatened to break, Tomás climbed the face of the avalanche before realizing he would need to push his board up and over the wave in order for it to clear the top of it. About half way up the face, he slid off the tail of his board and pushed hard, hoping he would find the board on the other side as he swam through the wave that was an Olympic-sized swimming pool wide. Surfacing, he could feel the breaking wave that had passed tugging at him, threatening to drag him along with it. But there was no time to consider that wave—another, bigger wave was nearly upon him.

Exhausted and unwilling to swim through this wave, he instead paddled over the top. The wind gusted hard at the peak of the wave before he fell endlessly behind it, landing so hard that the fiberglass on his board cracked, leaving what surfers call "stress fractures" throughout the board. Then Tomás saw a wave so vicious he hoped to never see another like it. As he paddled toward the horizon, he could feel the wave pulling him toward it as it sucked all the water from the reef and he fought the sick panic that rose within while wondering if something still bigger lurked behind this mountain. If so, he would surrender his lifeless body to the sea without further resistance. His only other choice was the madness of trying to ride the approaching wave.

Spinning around he took long, hard strokes, rose to his feet as the wave jacked behind him and the offshore wind gusted like a firehouse. The wave sucked still more water from the reef until it exposed lava boulders not far beneath the surface. The wall went vertical and then concave, and even he, one of the best surfers on the coast, had no chance against it. He was only about ten feet down the face when the board slid out from under him. "God no," shouted Max from the boat, in a prayer that echoed the heavens as his brother's board and body fell and the entire Pacific unloaded, the board held down like a toothpick before shooting back up, thirty feet or more above the wave's crest, now in two nearly equal halves. The pieces fell before being eaten by the whitewater and eventually vomited up onto the lava cliffs where they would be ground like course sand.

Beneath the broken wave, Tomás was tumbled into blackness, each joint aching as he felt the power threaten to dislocate his limbs. He told himself to keep calm until he could no longer listen to that rational voice and began clawing up toward the thick aquatic clouds above him. But the clouds proved impenetrable, and he was pushed back into darkness again where he was forced to wait for the storm of the broken wave to clear. He gave himself to the blackness of the deep without struggle, floating in the netherworld. This was easy for him, since this was not the first time he had died. He recalled his uncle's words from long ago: "If you're drowning, breathe water." He took in a cool, satisfying lungful and drifted off, memories of his childhood playing behind sealed eyelids like a newsreel. As the force of the wave decreased he drifted up lifelessly and as he did he awoke and his will to live returned. He could now see beyond the blackness, up beyond the grey, watery grave. Swimming for his life, he broke the surface and cleared the thick white foam that was neither air nor water but more resembled heavy snow. Breathing was nearly impossible until he cleared the foam away. Then he spat out most of the water in his lungs and deeply inhaled all the air in the vicinity before vomiting hard. His body was dead but his mind hung on, and he hoped and prayed there was not another wave like this behind the one he had just survived.

Max jumped from the boat with his board and paddled back toward the disaster, searching the churning water for signs of life until he saw the head of his brother being moved slowly forward by whatever strength remained in his limbs. Another wave broke behind Tomás, a bit smaller this time, but still twenty feet for sure, and Tomás again disappeared from view where he was tossed into blackness for an indeterminable amount of time. The next two waves in the set were mercifully smaller, and Tomás had less trouble getting beneath them. Suddenly the ocean quit moving and went lake flat. But calm water could be another enemy, as the water moving toward shore also has to move back out to sea in the form of a riptide that in this case was as strong as a Colorado River rapid. If this rip caught him, Tomás would be beyond anyone's reach. As Max paddled forward, he was unsure if he would find life. Then, suddenly he was there, Tomás swimming slowly toward him, exhausted before collapsing on Max's board as the two embraced weakly, teary eyed, paddling the board in tandem, back to the boat that bobbed, tiny in the distance.

The ocean continued mysteriously silent just long enough for them to make the boat. When they arrived they panicked to note that the extra gas cans they always carried had been washed overboard. With less than half a tank left, their chances of making it back to land seemed remote. It took three tries before the engine finally caught and they pulled anchor. As they began the ride back, the wind switched to onshore, and the ocean gave way to a rage they were blessed to have escaped. The ride home was more up and down than straight as they were tossed by the elements and nearly capsized several times. But this seemed easy compared to what they had been through, and they laughed and relived each wave until they ran out of fuel a few hundred yards from shore. Fortunately the tide moved in their favor and they were pushed toward the beach. Finally achieving the shallow water in the bay, they jumped over the side and walked the boat to the sand.

They pushed the boat forward until they touched precious land in the way early explorers must have, the way only those stuck at sea for long periods can appreciate. They pulled the worthy *panga* up onto the sand until they collapsed beneath the now dark sky, afraid of nothing, thankful for everything, especially solid ground, especially life, especially each other.

# Behold

# Chapter 10

# PURGATORY

*There are some solitary wretches who seem to have left the rest of mankind, only, as Eve left Adam, to meet the devil, in private.*
*– Alexander Pope*

To say Tommy had changed during the past five years would be like saying the ocean changed when it awoke from being a placid body of water to one of life-threatening turbulence. It is the same body but with an entirely different look and character. There was nothing left of the cocky, ignorant boy Tommy. That child had disappeared and become Tomás, a hard muscled fisherman with hands so rough you could light a match on them. Gone was the paranoid dog of a scowl he gave everyone who tried to get close. And while he still rarely smiled, he generally wore the peaceful expression of those to whom the ocean reveals its secrets. On occasion there was enough happiness to boil over into laughter as he learned to care for something and someone other than himself. Through living closely with the elements, by observing Jose and Carmen, and by listening to the old priest in town, he had achieved a mustard seed of a faith that grew steadily in his soul.

He had never before trusted happiness, but now a measure of that emotion had found him. The great well of his hatred had mostly dried up. What was left was reserved for his father and for himself, thinking back to the day he had become a man's judge, jury and executioner. On occasion, he became so distant even his family could not reach him. But they knew to leave him alone and that within days the storm in his soul would clear, and he would join them as a good son and brother. In all this time, Tomás was rarely asked his secret and he never revealed it to anyone, not even Max. He only left

Santa Guadalupe to venture into town on occasion with Max, or with Jose when his leg bothered him too much to drive. Not once had he wanted to return to the U.S. Now that he had become an adult, however, he knew there were things left unfinished.

Carmen, the woman Tomás reverently called *Madre,* noticed a change in her son. While she had prayed endlessly for him, her fears were nonetheless realized when he told her he would be leaving home for a short time. Without another word, Tomás quietly packed scant supplies and walked into the mountains that surround Guadalupe. He continued south for three days with little water and no food. With only scorpions, coyotes, lizards, and buzzards for company, he camped beneath the star blanket each night, questioning his entire existence. While fear was not a big part of his makeup, he could not shake the terrifying idea that he would some day be torn from the home he loved, when the American Government or the *Federales* finally discovered where the murderer of Big Tom was living.

On his third day, Tomás deliriously walked through dry arroyos, over loose volcanic rock, up and down steep grades until darkness found him atop a dead cinder cone. There were no signs of civilization in any direction. At night the stars were close enough to touch and comets' tails spoke out among the great black expanse. Coyotes howled in the distance as he cleared rocks for a bed, looking up for hours, trying to clear his mind of everything, something impossible since it was filled with ten lifetimes of bad and now good memories. For the first time since his childhood, he cried. His tears were not for the death of his father, but the death of the boy he could have been. Realizing he could never be happy in the way other people were, he cursed the darkness and threw rocks at the troublesome stars. Within an hour, Tomás had exhausted all his tears and prayed sincerely for the first time since he was a little boy. He offered his knees to the rough terrain, and folded his hands, crying out and asking questions that men of earth only guess at: What is a man born for? Was I created for a reason? Is this world the result of an accident as my teachers long ago taught me? He made a bed of his supplies and a blanket from the extra clothing he had brought.

He slept hard for hours until he was woken by such deep coldness it seemed to be a living being. The morning, which had began freezing cold, was soon scorching hot. Wandering from his camp, he ate nothing but a few manzanita berries that day and found muddy water in a small pool that he lapped up before wandering the cliffs and crags, praying for answers that were locked away behind an iron door. Finally, with the three days of fasting and violent prayer behind him, Tomás broke through the door to discover some of the answers he was seeking—there was something/someone greater than himself who had made a sacrifice greater than he could ever imagine. He would give himself to that power, surrender to it, and let himself face his own crucifixion when the time came. He prayed as he walked home filled with resolve to do the one thing he had avoided since his youth. He would return to the U.S. in hopes that the criminal system there would return a manslaughter verdict. That was his only chance at true freedom.

The saddest day in the Santiago family's history occurred when Tomás told them he was leaving. They all took it hard, but Lupita ran from the house into the desert, where she hid from everyone and cried bitterly, before composing herself and returning indoors.

All the money that Tomás and the family made from the fishing business had been used just to stay afloat; there was nothing left for unimaginable expenses like attorneys, even though they and everyone in the village would make themselves dirt poor pitching in to free the Santiago boy, no matter what he needed.

While the family tried to pretend they would see Tomás again soon, everyone realized he was leaving for good. Nobody ate the homemade tamales made by Carmen and Lupita. Jose sat somberly in his rocker, lighting one cigarette on the last while staring into space. Max and Margarita arrived at the house early with their newborn daughter, Baby Carmen, as Max tried to distract himself by retelling his many adventures with his brother. When Lupita again ran from the house, Tomás ran after her, finding her alone in the cold night. Then it was like he saw her for the first time, and he knew he had loved her from the first. He touched her hand and drew her to himself and held her like he had never held another person in his life. Even with that he could not promise her he would return. His future was now in the hands of an American judge.

# Chapter 11

# AMERICAN ALIEN

*A Coyote is a smuggler of human flesh and usually a resident from south of the U.S./ Mexican border. Those with the least to give often pay all to a Coyote for the most dangerous trip in the world.*

Like anyone living near either side of the Mexican border, Tomás was partially aware of what it took to cross from Mexico into the United States. In his case, however, he was a U.S. citizen hoping to avoid arrest before arriving in the city of his birth, Newport Beach. He had watched many friends from Santa Guadalupe leave their families in tears as they were packed off with nothing but a sack lunch and a few hundred well-hidden U.S. dollars after paying non- refundable thousands to the Coyotes who offered passage into the U.S. Regardless of the method, the way was long and dangerous with no guarantees. It could require hours stuck in the trunk of a car with two others, jumping high fences, crawling in the dark through rocks, dirt and mud. There was the option of trying a midnight run in a *panga*, running without lights across the Tijuana border, over a treacherous reef known as Tijuana Sloughs, landing up the coast where the boat would be ditched on the shores of Point Loma, La Jolla, Del Mar or Encinitas. It could require burrowing through tight, unsafe tunnels that were dug on the Mexican side of the border and ended up in a house in San Ysidro.

There were heart-pounding pursuits through the brush by dogs and the U.S. Border Patrol or the self-appointed vigilante groups that hunted down border crossers on their own. There were also smugglers who took your money before playing both sides of the fence, turning you in to *La Migra*, keeping the cash, maybe collecting a reward while avoiding any chance of getting arrested for smuggling. This was only the beginning; once you arrived in the U.S.

you were forever in danger of being caught and deported back to your country of origin. Politicians fought over the lives of the workers. The options were: let them all in, deport them all, or design guest worker programs that opened paths to citizenship.

Unlike the U.S., the Mexican government did not offer a ride back home to fugitives caught on their land. Any American caught living in Mexico illegally could face two years in prison and unimaginably cruel consequences. It would be far worse for Tomás if he were caught in Mexico.

As was his recent habit, Tomás fell on his knees and prayed in the dark, before sunrise. It was three A.M., and that sickness of a cold, uncertain morning pressed in on him as he petitioned a God whose name he had recently learned for a safe crossing and freedom from the charge of murder. Crossing himself in the name of the Father, Son and Holy Spirit, he took the same deep breath he would have if facing a big wave. Coming to his feet he contemplated the challenge before him, packing his things while realizing he had none of the documents required to enter the U.S. He had left that country even before he was old enough to drive. Many of those crossing the border illegally into the U.S. had identification, though much of it had been printed in a shop in Tijuana. With no license, passport, visa or Social Security number he would need to be extra careful. His advantages were being fluent in both English and Spanish and knowing what areas to avoid as an illegal immigrant since he had once illegally crossed from the U.S. into Mexico. As he left his house prepared to walk the twelve miles to the main road and hitchhike the remaining hundred miles to the border, the truck was waiting with Max huddled against the cold inside.

In the cab of the truck, Max clung to his brother for a long time, saying he would go with him all the way to the end, into the U.S. and even into prison if necessary. No matter how he pleaded, however, Tomás insisted he do this alone and finally convinced Max to drive him only as far as the border. He needed to stay home and look after the family.

As they drove, Tomás reflected on his life since meeting the Santiago family. He recalled the many lessons taught by Jose, the great swells, the big fish, his love for Carmen and now Lupita, and how Max and Margarita had married at the little church where Tomás stood up as his best man. Later, an entire cow was butchered and cooked on hot coals in the ground overnight, along with many large fish and vegetables of various kinds. The fiesta lasted three days, the wedding party loudly parading from house to house, blasting off firecrackers and occasionally firing pistols in the air as they went in celebration of the young couple.

Max drove his brother all the way to the Tijuana border while trying to persuade him not to leave. Regardless of his best arguments, however, Max knew there was no talking Tomás out of anything he set his mind to. Tomás was silent, focused only on his road ahead. Finally, approaching the line to cross the border, Max handed his brother a new leather wallet containing 200 American dollars, all in twenties.

"I won't need this," said Tomás, attempting to hand the money back to Max.

"You take it, or I'll pound you like I used to do," said Max.

Tomás finally took the wallet and said, "I'll be home in a week, two at the most."

"If you're not, I'm coming after you."

The men embraced tightly while holding back tears. Tomás broke free from the embrace, turned and set his face north, to cold fear and uncertainty while behind him, to the south, everything was warm and good.

At home the Santiago family lit candles, prayed rosaries and offered small items to the Sacred Heart of Jesus for Tomás. Lupita lifted the small golden cross from her neck, kissed it and pleaded with God to bring him home to her, soon. At that same moment, Tomás was longing for her even more than for his own life. He considered returning to her, but realized he would not be good for her or anyone until he had settled things in the U.S., even though settling them meant he would most likely forfeit what remained of his life.

# Behold

# Chapter 12

# DEAD AND ALIVE

*The U.S. Border Patrol recently uncovered the remains of 463 migrants in the U.S. desert.*

Tijuana was even more frantic and crowded than it had been when Tomás was there five years earlier. There were new buildings in the center of town and drywall mansions on the outskirts while the cardboard and plastic wrapped slums still lurked in the distance. Tomás, who had not seen television since he left the States, knew nothing of the drug wars waged in this town. If he had seen TV, he would have known of the tunnels built from Tijuana into the U.S. by smugglers, the violent clashes with police. He could not have known of the murderous underground or the bodies deposited amid the trash in the city dump or sent to the bottom of the sea. He noted the despair on the faces of the merchants on *Avenida Revolución* and the usually cheerful mariachis that, with a decreasing number of tourists to hear their music, wore threadbare uniforms, wandering the streets, playing songs nobody would hear. He was nearly run over by a taxi and sprayed with exhaust as the cab raced beyond him. Unable to find the rhythm of the hyperactive city, he attempted moving to a beat gone mad.

He was close enough to the border to see the U.S. with even rows of traffic moving easily and the long lines crossing from Mexico into the States with impatient honking drivers competing for a better spot.

The streets were lined with booths selling Mexican blankets, pottery and velvet paintings while street vendors stood between lines of cars, arms loaded with churros, and various trinkets. There were also children who cleaned car windows and then demanded money of the driver.

Once at the front of the line, a U.S. officer checked your car and asked questions. If you went into secondary, the interrogation area where you were sent if there was any suspicion about you or the items you were carrying, agents would tear your car apart while the drug-sniffing dogs did their best to locate whatever dumbness you might be trying to squeeze through. If they found Tomás trying to cross, it would be all over for him. Walking across the border was even riskier than driving since the officers checked you closely.

Tomás walked toward the border until he found a man waiting by the side of the road in a produce truck that was suspiciously empty. Taking a chance, he approached the man and asked if he would smuggle him across for fifty dollars. "Five hundred," the man answered coolly in Spanish.

"All I have is two hundred," Tomás replied.

"Meet me here in two hours." The negotiations over, the man asked Tomás for fifty dollars, which he said was for gas. After the man drove away, Tomás spent the next two hours wandering the streets, realizing he did not fit in here and maybe didn't fit on the other side of the border either. Two hours passed slowly and when he returned the man was not there. The man never did return so Tomás went looking again, until he found someone who was leaving for the border right then and would take him along.

"How's your English?" asked the Mexican man.

"I was born in the States."

"One hundred dollars U.S., and you ride up front with me, but don't say a word, unless spoken to. If they ask, say your wallet was stolen in Tijuana."

Tomás paid the driver and before getting into the passenger seat of the truck, spotted the man to whom he had given the original fifty dollars. Running from the truck he was in, he found the man, grabbed him by his shirt, shaking him and demanding his money back. He replied that he had spent most of it, and returned a five and a ten. That would have to do.

The new driver honked his horn and waved Tomás into the

rickety truck. Tomás jumped into the front seat and they waited in line. What he didn't know was that in the truck's bed, directly behind him, between rows of crates barely big enough for one person were three other passengers stacked up and waiting to get across for the chance at a job in the U.S., any job.

The border crossing was slow and the exhaust from this and other old trucks was suffocating. They were in line for over an hour when, finally at the border, the U.S. agent looked into the truck's cab and asked the driver some questions. Turning to Tommy, which was the name he would again use in the States, he asked his residence. He hesitated for a moment before saying U.S. The agent asked him to get out of the car and spoke with Tommy for a while, demanding to see some identification. "I was held up in Tijuana and they took everything," he said.

"What were you doing in Mexico?" asked the agent.

"Just looking around."

Tommy's story wasn't perfect, but his English was and when the agent punched his name into the computer, nothing came up and he was sent back to the car. Now the agent inspected the truck's cargo. One of the boxes was opened and when the border guard found nothing but Mexican pottery he waved the truck through.

Immediately the U.S. road felt different, a velvet carpet with none of the violent bumps encountered to the south. The smuggler drove about a mile, pulled off into a residential area and let Tommy out without a word. Then he opened the bed of the truck and freed the three passengers who looked around before scampering toward the highway. Each was on his own–the three Mexican men seeking mere survival, while Tommy hoped to find his way back to Orange County, where he would turn himself in for the murder of his father.

He offered the man another fifty dollars to take him further. The man agreed and drove him forty-five minutes north to the town of Encinitas, a place that had obviously been founded by Spanish speaking people, the name itself meaning "Little Oaks" in Spanish. After being dropped off in Encinitas, Tommy took his last few dollars and walked into a fast food dump where he ordered a hamburger, fries and a drink. A fat man with a sleeve of mismatching tattoos was seated in a booth near him, eating lunch as if by osmosis while speaking on a cell phone, shouting, "I can't go surfing now, I'm waiting for my Mexicans." Tommy, who silently prayed against his own fury, realized that many good Mexican people endured this sort of ignorance and more, every day. While there was no excuse for it, the same things happened to Americans on the other side of the border. Then he remembered the words of his father, Jose, "Prejudice is a dog that bites everyone." But not everything named prejudice really was—most people simply related to and trusted things that were like them. Prejudice was nothing. Prejudice was everything. Prejudice was a dog that bit its own tail and eventually ate itself. Thinking of his adopted family and now considering himself Mexican, he disliked the fat man. But he would have to save his emotions for his coming trial. He savored his food slowly, realizing it would likely be the last he ate for a long time. He pocketed packets of sugar and ketchup, so he could keep himself nourished on the road until he found something better to eat. As he walked out to the street, he saw the Mexican day-workers lined up on Encinitas Boulevard. They could have been his family from Santa Guadalupe, a place he considered home and longed to return to. But he had to accomplish his mission, regardless of what he wanted.

His hardships had not only taught him to live like a man, but also a wild animal when needed, keenly aware of anything that resembled food. Walking back through town, he fished out a discarded sandwich from the trash. Also along the road were natal plums growing on a hedge that he picked and ate. On the ground were pine nuts that fell from trees. The cliffs were lined with wild spinach, radish and cactus which produced two types of edible fruit: *nopales* and prickly pear. He harvested the vegetables along with a few dozen mussels from the reef. Washing the wild vegetables in the saltwater he made a small stick fire to cook the muscles. After eating his fill there was enough food remaining to feed the seagulls, so he shared his feast with the pesky birds.

He had been to this beach before and ridden good waves here. It was called Swami's after the temple on the cliff, home of Self Realization Fellowship, founded in the 1940s by a guru known as Paramahansa Yogananda. The reef at Swami's offered a good wave that peaked outside into a perfect A-frame, with a fast little walled up racetrack further inside. The last time he surfed was at the point in Guadalupe where the waves were six to eight foot, hollow and glassy, where he and Max were the only surfers within fifty miles. He now watched in wonder as forty surfers battled each other for scraps. He fell asleep in the warm sun, dreaming he was home with the Santiago family. He slept that night without apparent dreams beneath the Swami's lifeguard tower, sharing the enclosure with a few homeless men.

For three days he walked the roads and camped in the bushes adjacent to the freeways. Since his fieldworker hat, rugged clothing and darkly tanned skin made him look like a migrant worker, he had little luck hitchhiking. Eventually he found a good Samaritan among the righteous, and one ride deposited him, dirty and exhausted, on the steps of the Santa Ana Courthouse.

Even in this place that held many poor people, he looked like the poorest among them. Locating the appropriate window, the clerk shoved the necessary paperwork before him and stared vacantly as Tommy recited his confession. Without really listening, the man, who smelled of greasy french-fries and cigarettes assumed the young man before him was an illegal trying to apply for citizenship. When, after numerous explanations, the man finally understood Tomás' meaning, he grabbed the paperwork from him, and pointed across the street to the six-story jail. Tomás expected to spend the next few months there awaiting trial, before being transferred to a State Prison where he would spend the next few decades and maybe the remainder of his life.

At the police station, Tommy told the entire story for the first time, leaving out none of the details. Expecting to be arrested, Tommy was instead told there was nothing on his record and that he was free to go home. Furthermore, they could find no report of a man being murdered on or around the mentioned date, named Tomas Sinclair Sterns.

The pronouncement meant that Tommy was free to go and that Big Tom had survived the blow to the head and was still alive; out there somewhere, ready to crush someone's life in the way he had nearly done his only son's. There was no relief in the revelation that his father was alive, and Tommy considered either giving up the quest for vengeance or returning to the only real home he had ever known in Guadalupe. He could marry Lupita and live peacefully or finish the job on his old man, doing the world a favor by keeping him from ruining other lives. Twisted by years of hatred, pain, and abuse, Tommy decided that nobody would ever pay for the old man's misplaced rage the way he had.

The best surfer from Newport Beach, the one whose aborted career should have been celebrated in movies and magazines, on the A-list for every club, curled up alone in the sand that night. Anyone who saw him then would have assumed he was a bum. That morning he ate a gourmet meal someone had discarded in a trashcan. He washed that down with water from a garden hose. He walked four blocks, not even bothering to look toward the beach breaks he had grown up surfing, nor wanting to see any of the surfers he knew from his childhood. In the Army/Navy Surplus store on Coast Highway, he committed his first crime in years by stealing a large hunting knife that he hid in his belt behind his back and covered with his shirt. As a fisherman, he had become deadly with knives and could filet a man's flesh like a fish in one quick slice.

He walked out past the surf shop and looked in to see an older TK who gave a friendly nod, no doubt mistaking him for a gardener. He continued moving forward without his old sponsor realizing this was his top team rider from years ago.

It was 9:30 A.M. when he strolled to the trailer to see the dump he had grown up in, now cleanly swept with flowers out front and a new coat of paint. There was an immaculate new 9'6" longboard hanging in the rafters of the trailer's adjacent awning. The door was open and Tommy knocked lightly until a not unattractive middle-aged woman walked forward. It seemed somebody else was living there. Thinking the boy was seeking a handout, the woman stayed politely behind the safety of the screen door. Tommy waited at the door while she excused herself, walked back to the kitchen and returned with a day-old peanut butter and jelly sandwich, a bag of fruit and water in a plastic cup. She opened the screen door cautiously, and gave the offering to Tommy, hoping he would leave. "Is Tom Stern here?" asked Tommy politely.

"He's at work," replied the woman.

"Where does he work?" asked Tommy, surprised the old man was actually doing something. "

"Up at Robert August's factory in Costa Mesa, shaping boards," she said proudly.

"Any idea when he'll be home?"

"He usually shows up around supper time. Who shall I say called?"

"Nobody," said Tommy, reaching behind his back to feel the hilt of the knife before promising to return later.

As he walked away, Tommy unwrapped the food and swallowed it quickly before wandering the hot sand. He saw some kids he knew, all grown up now. There was Bobby, his bulging bicep highlighted by a tribal tattoo. He was still loud and obnoxious and trying to convince some giggly high school girls he was the best surfer in town. There were others also, but he didn't want to reacquaint himself with any of them. Nobody recognized him since he looked entirely different and the word had gone all over town after his strange disappearance five years earlier that his father had finally murdered him and set the body adrift between the river jetties on a falling tide where it would be devoured by sharks.

He walked the shore, invisible as the homeless, which he in fact was. Tommy observed the latest group of young gremmies who lined the sand, no longer with distain. He wished he could warn them against the horrors of the age, the drugs and alcohol that crouched at their doors. He could teach them how to tube ride and turn without all the excessive flapping that usually accompanied a gremmie's movement. He realized his words would have seemed like a joke to them, coming from a homeless farmworker.

Walking miles up the beach past Newport and Balboa Piers, he finally arrived at the famed bodysurfing spot, the Newport Wedge, which did what it always did by mashing unsuspecting bodysurfers into the sand on the moderate south swell. Tommy was not tempted to bodysurf the Wedge, as he had done years earlier or to ride those other waves that had once been the focus of his entire life. To him the entire place was dead and, without a heart, lacked the beat to hold it together. Yet, for the first time he noticed something good in his hometown. There were children and their parents joyfully enjoying the day together. There was goodness and even potential greatness among the masses.

It was twilight when he approached the trailer again; this time hearing country music turned down low on a tinny radio as his father's voice, somehow softer, broke through. "Got some new orders in from Japan, and we should be busy until next summer," the voice said, hopefully.

Tommy knocked, and Big Tom approached the screen door. A faint glimmer of recognition appeared in his sad eyes before the old man refocused to see the somehow familiar looking illegal at his door. Big Tom was older, and the deep, ugly scar that had healed poorly on his forehead where Tommy had hit him with cast iron made him look older still. A surge of panic came over Tommy, and he felt like running away. But there was something in the old man's voice that was less bitter and hateful.

"Yes?" wondered Big Tom, who stood, blocking the entrance.

"It's me," was all Tommy could manage before pulling off his hat and looking the old man in the face for the first time in years.

"Tommy," was all the old man said, bowing his head in shame. "Come in."

All the hatred and rage surfaced in Tommy, who now stood nearly equal height to his father. He rested a hand on the knife behind his back again. Searching the old man's eyes, he could find nothing left worth killing. His eyes were clear, he was trim, and he walked steadily. Big Tom was sober.

"Tommy, this is my wife, Melisa. Melisa, this is my son, Tommy," said Big Tom softly, looking down, as the woman came forward and wrapped her arms around the younger Tom Stern.

"I've heard a lot about you," said the woman, smiling uncomfortably. Tommy did not reply, but pulled away and looked back into his father's face, hoping to locate the hatred he had for him. "Please sit down son," said Big Tom. Son, I…" Right then Big Tom let go a hundred years of tears that did not let up for minutes. Tommy said nothing.

Three plates of food were placed on the small dinner table. After a short blessing over the meal, the family ate in silence. Then, slowly the old man began speaking, not about that horrible night and the mistakes he had made, but about surfing. Big Tom was a child again, with childish dreams. There was so much to say and even more they could not say. Tommy could not hate him, but he would not love him. He had another father now, Jose, who had loved him when he did not deserve it and taught him all he needed to know. "Would you spend the night and go to San Onofre with me tomorrow morning, I've got an extra longboard and I thought we could…"

Tommy was offered a shower, a towel and a razor. Some of his old clothes had been kept in a drawer beneath the awning, and he picked out a flannel shirt and jeans from the stack. But he was not the boy who had left there years earlier, and the clothes no longer fit. Draping himself in a beach towel, he washed the clothes he had worn for days in the outside sink and dried them in the summer air on the porch. The next morning Tommy was up well before dawn, packing a few items into his worn out pack. Before leaving the master bedroom, Big Tom turned and kissed Melisa goodbye. Unlocking the truck he took the big, worn Bible from the passenger seat before opening the door for his boy, who got in and sat down.

# Behold

# Chapter 13

# HOMECOMING

*San Onofre is like a historic monument in California surfing, a place once ridden by surfing pioneers on great wooden boards. Names like Duke Kahanamoku, Guard Chapin, Eve Fletcher, Joyce Hoffman, Dorian Paskowitz, Ron Drummond, Tubesteak, Woody Ekstrom and Whitey Harrison would be at the top of the San Onofre Hall of Fame, if there were such a thing. Nothing much has changed since they first rode the place in the early 1900s, except for the surfboards that have gone from wood to foam and fiberglass. There's a parking lot, bathrooms and a nuclear power plant waiting menacingly, just to the south.*

*The ghosts of surfers past live on in the children, grandchildren and great grandchildren of the legends at San Onofre. Kids pay tribute to their forebears by cross stepping gracefully forward and hanging ten smoothly on their parents' heavy retro surfboards. Mostly it's a bunch of average surfers out having fun on average waves that require little effort to enjoy as they roll toward shore. It is not uncommon to see a five-year old join an eighty-something year-old veteran on the same wave.*

It was small and crowded at San O as Big Tom rolled in and was greeted by the Hawaiians, "Howzit, Tom?" He drove past the Point and Dog Patch, finally parking at Old Man's amid families of surfers, some still wet from dawn patrol, others embracing cups of hot coffee while contemplating the dropping tide.

That mid-summer morning at San Onofre was not much different than the one when Big Tom paddled his son out to catch his first waves, years earlier. The swells still rolled gently over the cobblestone reef as surfers gathered in the lineup and on shore. You could almost taste the aloha of days past as the offshore winds picked up the scent of sage and perfumed the beach and ocean for miles. The biggest difference between now and years earlier were the vastly increased crowds and that Ellen Stern, Tommy's mother and Big Tom's first wife was not there with wrapped sandwiches for her husband and her boy and anyone else who hungrily left the water for the warm sand. On occasion Ellen surfed with them also. All who observed the family noted their joy.

Somehow Big Tom's memory of Ellen had finally lost the power of pain. Not that it actually hurt any less, but the persistent sting had dulled as something redemptive and hopeful was placed in front of it. It was like all the stopped clocks had been rewound and the world was new again, while the deep and precious scar on the heart began to fade. On that new morning Big Tom paddled out slowly as a small wave broke in front of him, and he pushed his longboard beneath the playful whitewater. The sun was rising fast as he surfaced from the foam, cleared his eyes and squinted to see what looked like his son, Tommy, next to him, breaking through a wave smiling in the innocent way he had as a child. It was not his son, but a young boy full of hope and wonder as he approached the infinite ocean to ride some of his first waves. A wave rose outside and rolled in as the man and the boy paddled out to meet it. Without a word, the two were there, just as it had been a lifetime ago. They spun around, catching the wave before lightly moving over the water like flying fish, Big Tom reacting to the beat of the ocean, a rhythm planted deep in his heart in antiquity by a creator who loved him enough to offer the gift of water baptism. There were no walls to contain his worship, no song and no prayer that any person could hear.

Back on the sand, Big Tom stood alone, dried by the noonday sun. Without ever hearing him say goodbye he knew his son had left him again. Still he pleaded and half prayed, "Come home, son," to the cloudless sky, to himself, to the waves and the power behind them.

Father and son were physically far apart and thinking of each other while Big Tom knew and Tomás knew they would never see each other again on earth. As Big Tom stood in the San Onofre sun, his only son was scouring the fast food place in San Ysidro for a ride into Mexico. When he found someone to drive him across, he paid the man his last few dollars for the pleasure of crossing the border in the trunk of his car. Just beyond the Mexican side of the border, Tomás was released from the trunk of the car. He was now free to find his way to the place where the remainder of his heart beat for Lupita and the Santiago family.

It took half a day and two long rides before Tomás was again facing the dirt road where he would negotiate the twelve miles of dust and rocks leading home. It was dark when the light from the little house came into view. And the light was the light of the world. As the light showed the way and Tomás and his birth father approached their homes, a sense of wonder fell upon them.

Tomás entered the door of the Santiago house and his own heaven on earth just as his father held his chest and gasped for breath. A jolt of fear was followed by a burst of joy that Big Tom had not known since childhood. The joy rose in him and in his son from the depths of two great hearts as the big man fell to the floor. Father and son were propelled toward their rewards, one heavenly and one earthly at exactly the same moment.

# Behold

# TWICE TOLD TALES

## Good Things Love Water

Reading Instructions:

Get this book dirty. Take it to the beach, to Baja, or into the outback. Or, find a place you loved as a kid. If you can't do that, try your garage. The back seat of your car will do, or on your bed, especially if it's full of sand. Do not, under any circumstances, place this book on the coffee table next to pretty volume about "Napa's Wine Country." It is not to be read with shoes on, and you won't understand a word of it if your brain is being choked off by a tie.

## Kelea's Gift

Attention Anal-Retentives:
Earn Big-Money While Working At Home!

The first person to correctly identify a spelling error in this volume will receive my personal check for twenty-five cents.

# Behold

# KING OF
# THE SURF GUITAR

*When Dick Dale released his first album Surfer's Choice in 1962, it spawned a whole new genre of music. Now, over half a century later, his rock instrumental anthems continue to gain momentum. That's not the reason I admire him.*

–Originally published in *Kelea's Gift*

It's not my fault my father left the beach in Santa Monica and moved inland the year I was born. I had nothing to do with it, but I learned early on it's best to fess up to your venial sins before someone else discovers them. So here goes: In 1962 I was an inland gremmie–a hodad, a kook! Still I had high ambitions of becoming a great surfer, and the first step was to join the Monterey Park Surf Club, which consisted entirely of inlanders.

My brother Dave and I sat in the clubhouse ready to pledge allegiance as the secretary, Chickie, examined the clipboard in his hand and began the inquisition:

"How long have you been surfing? What is your favorite surf spot? Are you a good noserider? Do you ride big waves?"

We answered every question well enough to fool the others. Then Chickie hit us with a big one: "Who's the best surfer in the world?" Some of the club members whispered the name Phil Edwards. One guy said Dewey Weber. Butch Van Artsdalen and Donald Takayama received honorable mention. "Who's the best surfer in the world," demanded Chickie again. Dave and I huddled up for a moment before emerging with a united voice, saying–"Dick Dale."

"Dick Dale's a hodad," laughed Chickie. The other club members were divide–some saying Dale really was the best while others agreed with Chickie that he was in fact a hodad. Nobody in that group could deny, however, that he was the hottest guitar player we had ever heard. Turns out neither Dave nor I made the cut and suffered the fate of having to ride waves without those guys to cut us off.

It was our older sister Jackie who brought Dick Dale into our home, and the music pumped the newly discovered feeling my brother and I had recently found in surfing. Here was the stoke like a big north swell, and I spent long hours land locked, carpet surfing to "Surf Beat," "Miserlou" and "Mile Zero." I set the record cover atop the hi-fi, to imitate the photo taken of the king as he slid a Dana Point wall.

I was in ninth grade and had never been to a surfer stomp when Jackie asked if I wanted to go to Harmony Park to see her favorite band, *Dick Dale and His Deltones*. I wore my Madres plaid shirt, white Levis and Converse tennis shoes. The band tore it up that night as surfers, phonies, hodads and gremmies united on the dance floor without knowing who could surf or who could not.

Twenty years later a young surfer named Chris O'Rourke is living and dying with Hodgkin disease at a home in Encinitas, California, when the idea of a musical fundraiser comes up, to help pay for mounting medical expenses. The La Paloma Theater generously donated their Encinitas facility, as did some of the talented local musicians. Every San Diego radio station lent their support with free airtime as surfers from Imperial Beach to Oceanside scraped up five bucks for a ticket.

I think it was World Surfing Champion Peter Townend who gave me Dick Dale's phone number. Before dialing the phone I recalled my gremmie years, lying awake three nights in a row after seeing him at Harmony Park and later the Rendezvous as the moves of the surfer stomp were revived in my memory.

He answered the phone himself and listened patiently as I, a complete stranger, stumbled through introductions, and revealed that one of California's best surfers was fighting for his life. He heard me out before informing me that he couldn't attend. His wife was having surgery on the date of the concert, and he needed to be at her side, he said. He hoped I would understand; he just couldn't make it. I thanked him for his time and hung up.

A few minutes later Dick Dale called back to say his wife had rescheduled surgery in order to play the benefit. He, she and the entire band would play the La Paloma for free. I can still recall the force of his words as he added, "Any surfer who won't spend five dollars to help this kid isn't worth the wax he stands on!"

Dick Dale and his band rocked the joint hard. After the show I introduced myself to him backstage and he said he hoped he had helped the cause. The band broke down their instruments, returned to the tour bus where they and Dick Dale vanished like the super hero he is. Our grateful town was left vibrating in his wake and I realized that Dick Dale was not only the king of the surf guitar and no hodad, but in my mind, the greatest surfer who ever lived.

# SKIP AND DONNA, A LOVE STORY
# (For the Most Part)

*With nearly sixty years of daily surf time, it is doubtful that any surfer in the world has traveled more linear feet on a surfboard than Skip Frye. While he battles aquatic elements, Skip's wife Donna takes on environmental battles from shore.*

–Originally published in *Joyrides*

It was in a time of famine when Skip and Donna found themselves looking for each other without really knowing it. The blond, tanned surer had walked into the restaurant she was dining in, and Donna thought he looked nice. He was unlike the other men she had recently met in her Pacific Beach home. The two found themselves paying their bills at the counter together when she managed the courage to say hello. Conversation came slowly and deliberately from the thoughtful Frye. *Maybe he doesn't like me,* she thought. Then again… When she took a chance and asked him to stop by her house for dinner the following night, he accepted.

Skip arrived on time, and as Donna would soon realize was his way, spoke little. He simply sat in the front room watching the weather on TV, paying close attention to a certain hurricane that might blow waves into his home break, PB Point. From the kitchen, Donna could see him, politely following the storm. He was not at all like the other men she had met recently.

Time passed, and he sat without comment as she continued

preparing the evening meal. *Maybe he doesn't like me;* the thought was hard to shake. *Maybe he's a vegetarian, and he won't eat the steak I'm making.* She convinced himself that he must be shy. A shock came minutes later when from the corner of her eye she saw this stranger, this animal, removing his pants in her front room. Not even the worst of them had done that.

Donna picked up a frying pan, holding it tightly behind her back, ready to discharge or smash her guest if necessary. By the time she made the front room, he had removed his pants. There he stood, the great Skip Frye in salt-encrusted red, nylon trunks as Donna tried to hide the cast iron skillet behind her back. "It's really hot in here," muttered the surfer as the cook hid her metallic weapon behind her back, smiled and stammered that dinner was ready.

Somehow Skip and Donna got through the time of courtship, fell deeply in love and have remained that way for quite some time.

*Skip and Donna Frye were married in a quiet ceremony on December 22, 1990. They continue to live in Pacific Beach, California where Skip surfs, makes surfboards and tends to matters of the soul. After years as a city councilwoman, Donna has earned the reputation as a fighter of corruption and someone not to mess with in or near her home.*

# MURPHY'S LAW

*I first heard of Jack "Murf the Surf" Murphy through Surfer Maga-*
*zine. The next time I read about him was in the* Los Angeles Times
*where he was pictured handcuffed and facing a long prison term.*

–Originally published in *Kelea's Gift*

To my left is a mountain of a man with his blue denim shirt unbut-
toned, revealing a swastika that makes a ten-inch journey down his
cut abdomen. Directly below the swastika, lining his iron waist, are
the words: "White Power." To my right are two African American
men equal in stature to the neo-Nazi. They eye White Power and me
closely. Two armed-guards pace a catwalk twenty-some feet above
us, but a world away. A sign directly above us reads, "No warning
shots." If something starts it might not end without blood.

  We are in the maximum-security section of Donovan State
Prison, and these men, along with a few hundred others who have
been convicted of violent crimes, are gathered to hear America's
most famous jewel thief, Jack "Murf the Surf" Murphy, speak about
his fast times.

  I am here because of a call from world-famous surfer, David
Nuuhiwa, who is visiting inmates as Murf's guest, and part of Bill
Glass's Weekend of Champions, a group that attempts to bring the
light of the gospel into our national hellholes on an almost week-
ly basis. Earlier, Tino Wallenda, a key member of America's most
famous high-wire family, revealed how his father fell over 100 feet
to his death. Later, Wallenda will walk the wire for the prisoners,
lecturing them about their own mortality, as he tiptoes with death,
shielded from eternity by nothing but a quarter-inch cable. The act

will get the attention of the men who have risked their lives for other reasons–anger, revenge, drugs, money. The words of Sandi Fatow, who once traveled with Jimi Hendrix, became involved with the Miami underworld and hit bottom as a Harlem junkie before making the same U-turn Murphy and his band of gypsies have taken, seem to penetrate. All the storytellers have one thing in common– they have damaged their lives and found redemption from their private hells.

But it's Murphy they have come to see–hoping to hear the stories of prison riots, mega scams, and pulling the biggest jewel heist in history. They will not be disappointed.

Sixty-two year old Jack Roland Murphy bounces onto the stage like a teenaged inmate jacked on meth. I know a little about his early days–how he grew up surfing in Carlsbad, California in the '50s with famed surfers L.J. Richards and Phil Edwards before moving with his family to Pittsburg where he held a chair as a violinist with their philharmonic orchestra, even before graduating high school. His athleticism earned him a tennis scholarship from the University of Pittsburg, and eventually a gig as an acrobat and high-tower diver with the Barnum and Bailey Circus. But the boy wanted to surf again, and the Pittsburg winters drove him south to Florida, where he discovered warm water and good waves at places like Sebastian Inlet. Within a few years he was considered the East Coast's top surfer, winning the state championships in the early '60s. But Miami held other attractions for a smart, athletic kid, and there was easy money to be made.

One night Murf and an accomplice made their way to the back lot of the New York Museum of Natural History. Patiently waiting for the guards to complete their rounds, they climbed over a steel spiked fence that dropped down into a sunken courtyard next to a large, dark building. Scaling several chain-linked fences, they eventually reached the 125-foot wall where they climbed cautiously, maneuvering their way up to a narrow ledge that wrapped itself around the building, five floors up. They were directly over the J.P. Morgan

Gem Room, just as they had planned. They entered a research lab on the top floor through an unlocked window where Murf secured the end of the 125-foot rope he carried with him. Lowering the rope down to their final destination, the pair silently cascaded to the gem room.

The next five hours are a joyous romp in the park for Murf and his partner. By early morning, the cat burglars have lifted the Midnight Sapphire, the largest black sapphire in the world, the De-Long Ruby, the world's most perfect star ruby, the Eagle Diamond, the largest diamond ever found in America and twenty-three other precious gems, including the ultimate prize, the Star of India, the largest star sapphire in the world, with a mysterious 300-year history. That night, Murf and his partner celebrate at the Metropolitan Jazz Lounge in Times Square where legendary drummer, Gene Krupa is performing with his band. Nudging the drummer, Murf quips, "Krupa, you'd never guess what I've got in my pocket." Krupa, who has seen it all, is blown away at seeing the multi-million dollar gemstone resting in Murf's hand like a set of car keys. Together, they roll down to Greenwich Village where they sit with Herbie Mann for a jazz session at the Village Gate.

Thugs, thieves, rapists and murderers are dead silent. Murf the Surf is a big prison celebrity whom they respect, just as their predecessors did George Meyer, "The Devil's Driver," a penitent gangster who had once wheeled the getaway car for Al Capone during the bloody Saint Valentine's Day Massacre. Having served two decades in similar joints, Murphy understands the volatile nature of the men before him. Still, he shows no fear of them. "You think you're tough? You're not tough," he says as I look for a safe exit, quickly realizing there are none. The Nazi tightens his jaw. Others assume threatening postures, intent on proving Murphy wrong.

To illustrate true toughness, Jack tells the story of a man who was nailed to a cross and never made a sound. He tells them how the man took the rap for them. Of course there's the story of the big jewel heist and his subsequent confinement. He tells how within one year he's back in prison again, this time for a long stretch that multiplies when he leads the biggest prison riot in Florida history. By the time Murphy's rebellion is spent, he's looking at double life plus twenty years. The story of his parole is just part of his miracle.

In time the outlaw portion of his life would be turned into a popular movie and proves the inspiration for television's jewel heist genre. What Murphy considers the real story, however, his conversion, has been largely left undocumented by mainstream media.

The show is over, and I relax along with the Nazi's facial muscles. Everyone has listened politely, and most drift numbly back to reading books or writing letters in their cells. Of those who stick around, there is a man convicted of killing his wife. He tells a counselor on hand, "I haven't cried in twenty-five years, and now I can't stop." Another man asks some difficult questions concerning the fairness of God. The support team, along with Murphy, prays for him and a dozen or so others. Some men try unsuccessfully to hold back tears as they hear Bible passages first memorized a lifetime ago, in a child's Sunday school class.

An inmate asks Murphy "What are you doing here? When I get out, I'm never coming back." Murphy replies, "I'm an expert in doing time; I served over twenty-one years. Since then I've been to over 1,200 different prisons, and I've found that it doesn't matter if you're behind bars or not. If you're not doing God's business, you're still just doing time."

These days find Jack Murphy on the road with a gang of some of the baddest criminals this country has ever confined. These are the same types of pimps, prostitutes and hustlers Jesus Christ embraced 2,000 years earlier. Also on the roster are NFL stars, a world-class ventriloquist and a biker gang. Countless previously thrown away lives are redeemed, and thousands enjoy true freedom because of the experience Murf the Surf calls "The most exciting thing I've ever done in my life." Coming from him, that's saying something.

*All the guys liked Sarah Jane, and she had no trouble borrowing a surfboard.*

# SARAH JANE

–Excerpt from *Twilight in the City of Angels*

One Saturday morning I rode my bike to the park to hunt tadpoles. There, I saw a pretty girl who had a jar filled with the tadpoles and small fish she had caught. Someone said her name was Sarah Jane. She was one year older than me, very tall, and had white-blonde braids, light skin, and freckles. Sara Jane was what we then called a "tomboy," and it was rumored she could throw a curve ball that broke almost a foot before landing right over the plate nearly every time. She was a better kickball player than any of the boys, and I would soon discover she was also a great surfer.

After hunting tadpoles with her, she invited me to her house. In her backyard was a tipi she had built and often slept in. Next to the tipi was a cage she had built out of scrap wood and glass. The cage was divided into sections containing snakes, lizards, and horned toads that she called by the Latin name *insectivorous iguanid lizards*. She also had cages made of chicken wire for baby birds that had fallen from their nests, keeping them alive with eyedroppers filled with mashed worms. She had three glass aquariums—one for fish, one for crickets, and one for mice. The mice and crickets she fed to her snakes. Sarah Jane was not Catholic and did not go to Veronica's, but to the public school, Bell Junior High.

One day, we were playing stretch with her knife in her backyard when her mother called her into the house for dinner. She told me to stay in the tipi, and she would see me later. After dinner, she came to the tipi with some chicken and corn wrapped in a napkin. As I ate, we planned to tramp into the local hills the next morning and agreed to meet at my parents' house. I left Sarah Jane and stayed with my parents that night and was up before light, packing a lunch and filling my father's war canteen with Kool-Aid. I sat on the porch to wait for her as the sun came over the hills. It wasn't long before she came bouncing high down the center divider of the street on her pogo stick, braids flying. That pogo stick was her main form of transportation and she bounced on it all over town–to the library, down Main Street, through the shopping centers, and even to school when it was in session. She was moving fast and bouncing high until she turned up onto our sidewalk and followed the cement path to the porch where I was waiting for her. She made one extra hard bounce before vaulting from the pogo stick, and her big, moccasin-covered feet landed on the ground right next to me. She laid the pogo stick down carefully in the ivy near the porch in the front yard.

We sat on the porch surveying her home-drawn map of the hills while I strapped my hunting knife to my belt and slung the bow Jose had made for me over my shoulder, along with the leather sheath filled with arrows he had also hand crafted.

It was a sunny day as we hiked up the grade on Wilcox Avenue to the dirt path that led up into the hills. The path was filled with rabbits that sprang out from beneath our feet as we walked, and I shot wildly at them, missing each one as they sprinted into bushes or holes where we did not see them again. With the binoculars Sarah Jane's father had taken from a dead German officer in the war, she always spotted the rabbits before I did. When she whispered, "Stop," I would freeze in my tracks, and she would hand me the binoculars to see the rabbit clearly. She taught me to move slowly on the balls of my feet, like an Indian, to where the rabbit was sitting. I would shoot at it and miss every time.

Owls, hawks, pheasants, and mud hens were the targets of my arrows, but I never landed any of them. As morning progressed, rabbits and other animals became scarce. I caught a horned toad with my hand and put it into the shoebox Sarah Jane was carrying. She punched holes in the top of the box with her knife and stuffed the box with grass and a few bugs to keep it alive until she got home to put it into a cage. She caught a tree frog, and then a few moments later, a small garter snake that I wouldn't touch, convinced it was a rattler. When I saw the snake was harmless, I held it nervously while its upper body twisted around my arm. Sarah Jane tried to force the frog into the snake's mouth, but the snake kept squirming out of my hand. The snake wouldn't hold still and eat the frog, so she let both go free in the bushes by a little pond of slimy green water where a million tadpoles were sprouting tiny new legs, ready to become frogs. We left the shoebox with the horned toad hidden in a tumbleweed near the pond.

I wandered from the path as another rabbit darted off from under my feet. I shot at the little cottontail, just missing. It ran away into the cactus patch before I could get another arrow out of my sheath. The rabbit had a limp and I was able to catch up by running as fast as I could, keeping an arrow pulled tightly against the string. I found the rabbit on a small, grassy mound a few feet away from the cactus patch, its back turned, eating grass quietly, unaware I was pointing an arrow at its heart. The arrow flew fast and straight, running through the rabbit's back and coming out the gut, pinning it to the ground. It squirmed in the dirt, twisting and turning, trying to get free of the arrow. I ran up closer and shot again, hitting it high on the back leg this time. I was laughing and shouting for Sarah Jane as she ran up the hill after me, breathing hard.

Holding out her knife, she offered to finish off the little rabbit, saying we could use the fur to make slippers. Taking her knife, I was about to kill the rabbit myself until I got close enough to see the baby cottontail jerking around, trying to free itself from my arrows. Its snow-white fur turned red from blood as it accused me with its little pink eyes, and I started crying. Sarah Jane did not hesitate and took back her knife, pushing it into the rabbit's neck, killing it quickly and wiping the knife blade clean on the grass.

"Come on Jack, let's skin it," she said happily. But I was still crying and dropped my bow in the dirt. Meanwhile she was sharpening her knife on her whetstone, and she shrugged her shoulders as I looked at her. Then she picked up the dead rabbit, put it onto a flat rock, cut out the guts, and skinned it. She threw the guts into the cactus patch, wrapped the meat in the wax paper she took from my sandwich, and dropped the soft, still quivering flesh into a paper bag she had with her for just such purposes. She wiped the knife blade clean of blood again and walked over to the cactus patch to lop off a few red prickly pears. She skinned the wild fruit and cut away the fine needles. We sat and ate the juicy prickly pears along with our sandwiches, followed by Kool-Aid in silence. "Be bold," I said to myself, remembering the courage of Jose as we continued tramping through the hills. If I found another rabbit I would kill it and skin it myself.

Hiking up over the hills, we eventually arrived at the reservoir and balanced along its narrow rock rim, making our way down to wade through the cold, shallow water. We could see the tall adobe walls of Mission San Gabriel in the distance. A woman was singing a Mexican song, cooling herself by standing in the shallows of the San Gabriel River, right where I had seen baby turtles and caught crawdads in a coffee can years earlier with Jose. There were no turtles or crawdads this time, but the water was clean and refreshing to drink. We drank from the stream and filled the canteen and Sarah Jane asked me to follow her as we hiked up past the place called "Rabbit Hill" on her map. To get there we had to walk through "The Plateau," beyond "The Grove of Palms" to a place called "The Big Desert," as they were labeled on her map. There was sand in the Big Desert, and, true to its name, nothing grew there. After passing through the sand onto hard ground again, we quietly treaded on the balls of our feet to a place with a few trees called "Hobo Camp." There, she showed me how to cup my hands near my ears to hear better and how to put water on my nose to wet it like a wolf, which would help me better smell any animals hiding in the hills.

At Hobo Camp, we hid in the bushes and watched the hobos from a safe distance. In a small grove of trees, three men huddled around a fire beneath an old worn out blanket hanging overhead in the tree branches as protection against the sun. Two of the men sat in the shaded dirt and one squatted beyond the shade of the blanket, turning his sunburned face directly to the sun. Empty tin cans, broken milk and beer bottles, and newspapers littered the ground near a rock fire pit near several rolled up blankets. Each of the hobos was ragged and dirty. The shortest among them had blond, curly hair and a blond, scruffy beard with some red in it. The one they called "Big Jim" was a giant hobo with dark skin, black stubble, and fresh blood over one eye. The man seated in the sun was short and skinny wearing a hat down over his face, so I could not tell what kind of a man he was. The food they were cooking in a rusty old can over a wood fire smelled awful, and the little hobo smoked and drank something from a tin can.

I whispered to Sarah Jane that I wanted to get out of there before we were discovered spying on the hobos. When she said she was staying, I decided to stay too. The little hobo tilted the can up to his mouth even after there was nothing left in it. Then, he threw the can angrily down onto the rocks.

The little hobo spoke, making his words stronger by waving his knife in the air, saying he was going to bust his friend out of jail as soon as he got a chance, and that nobody was a friend of his if they didn't help. The big hobo said they couldn't bust him out because there were too many cops around the jail and they would be caught. Hearing this, the little hobo said that the big hobo was no friend of his. Then the big hobo hit the little hobo hard in the face and the little hobo fell back onto the dirt. The little hobo charged the big hobo with a big stick. The big hobo took the stick from the little hobo's hand and quickly got him down where they wrestled on the dirt, rolling in our direction as the big hobo pounded the little hobo in the face.

They were getting close to our hiding place when Sarah Jane decided we should move on. We snuck away, again on our tiptoes, without being heard. Finally, we heard the little hobo yell that he gave up the fight, and we slipped off back down the hill unnoticed.

Soon everything was quiet except for the hobos, who yelled at each other and at the clear blue sky.

I peeked into the sack and smiled to see the pink, greasy meat of the rabbit. We walked for a long time and climbed a big steep hill, going through a tangle of trees until we came out onto a patch of thin, yellow dust. There, Sarah Jane dug in the dirt with her knife, surprising me when she came up with two petrified clams and one large petrified snail. She gave me one of the clams as a present and said the seashells in the hills proved the story of the great flood and Noah and the ark. She caught another horned toad but turned it loose in the bushes. When I asked why she let the horned toad go, she lifted her shirt, stuck out her belly, patted it, and said, "Pregnant."

We walked over the new green grass of the hills, holding hands through fields of large yellow flowers as high as our heads, small purple flowers only as high as our waists, and bamboo higher than a house. Arriving back at the trailhead, she picked up the horned toad in the box. The sun was setting on the old junked cars and the oil well as the hills glowed bright orange and gold. When the mosquitoes arrived, we ran down the hill together, laughing, smashing the insects against our arms and faces, hearing crickets and bullfrogs and the splashing of small fish in the pond competing for a meal of bugs.

Once beyond the pond, the mosquitoes were gone, and we walked slowly down the hill. Sarah Jane told me she had heard about a girl in my school named Maria who was pregnant. "Like the horned toad," she said, laughing and patting her stomach again. I let go of Sarah Jane's hand, punched her in the arm, and ran home alone. I watched through the front window as she retrieved her pogo stick from the ivy and somehow bounce home while carrying the horned toad.

The next day, after church I sat in the front yard alone, burning rows of ants with a magnifying glass when Sarah Jane came bouncing toward my parents' house on her pogo stick. I avoided eye contact with her as she bounced up the sidewalk.

Without a word she sat next to me and pulled the tiniest drumstick I had ever seen from the paper sack she was carrying, placing it on the grass between us. When I reached out for the chicken, she held my arm, saying, "Only if you say you're sorry for hitting me yesterday."

I apologized, and she released my arm so I could reach for the baby drumstick. "Well, how do you like your rabbit, Jack?"

"Jack rabbit," I said, laughing. "Jack rabbit . . . Get it? Jack . . . rabbit," I said, stupidly, before realizing we were eating the rabbit we had killed the day before. It tasted pretty good and I didn't complain about it.

The rest of my family had gone to the movies that afternoon. I was being punished for one thing or another and so was told to stay home. Sarah Jane and I went into the house and made cherry Kool-Aid, mixing it in the big tin pitcher with a wooden spoon, adding extra sugar and big chunks of ice. Back on the lawn, the little water drops slid down the sides of the brightly colored tin cups and we refilled our drinks until we had finished the entire pitcher of Kool-Aid, and the fried rabbit was nothing but bones. We lay there, looking up at the little sparrows in the oak tree, holding hands in the shade, protected from the hot afternoon sun.

I jumped up suddenly at hearing Donnelly shouting my name. I couldn't believe he had found my house; but, there he was, riding his bike, followed by Clank who had the length of bicycle chain he was named for wrapped around his knuckles. "Hey, Mexican, what are you doing with the Jew girl?" shouted Donnelly as they laughed, stopping to lay their bicycles against the curb, walking toward us. Sarah Jane and I were quiet as they moved close enough for us to hear their hard breathing.

"A beaner and a kike together," said Clank. "Jew girl," said Donnelly, spitting on the ground. Sarah Jane rose to her feet and stood her ground. Closing my eyes, I could hear Jose telling me to be bold. Sarah Jane stood up tall, and I straightened up next to her. Donnelly picked up a large sharp rock from the street and flung it at

Sarah Jane's head. She moved to one side as the rock whizzed past her. They had come a long way to find the new house, and I knew they would not leave without a fight. Sarah Jane was calm, touching the gold star around her neck. "My last name is Feinstein," she whispered to me while keeping her eye on them. "We're Jewish."

As Donnelly and Clank inched closer, she whispered from the side of her mouth. "Keep looking at them and don't be afraid, Jack."

"Be bold," I whispered to myself.

"Jack I'm gonna kick your ass," shouted Donnelly, Clank repeating Donnelly's promise while wrapping the chain tighter around his fist.

"Keep looking at them, Jack," repeated Sarah Jane, a little shaky this time. Slowly, keeping her eyes fixed on them, she reached down and picked up a big rock from the edge of the flowerbed, clenching the rock so tightly her fingers turned white. She was deadly with rocks and could hit whatever she aimed at. Inching forward, they would soon be upon us. Realizing we could not win, I turned and, as I ran, Donnelly yelled, "Look at the chicken shit Mexican run." Sarah Jane stood alone, raising her rock-filled fist, ready to hit whoever moved first. But she could only get one of them and they knew that.

Instead of retreating into the house, I ran to the garage and retrieved my bow and three arrows. When I returned to Sarah Jane's side Donnelly and Clank were close enough to touch. Inching forward, Donnelly pushed Sarah Jane who retreated a foot or so. If she fell they would rush us, but she continued standing. Donnelly was yelling and Sarah Jane was silent, holding tightly onto the rock. I lifted my bow and pulled the arrow tightly against the bowstring with the arrow pointed directly at Donnelly's heart.

Sara Jane pulled her shoulders back and continued facing them. "Get out of here, Donnelly, or I'll kill you," I said, feeling the power of Jose surging through my veins. They were silent now, and they didn't move forward or backward. All the hatred and fear in

Donnelly's eyes was focused tightly on me. The stupid Clank would follow whatever Donnelly did, right down to dying. "I swear to God, I'll kill you just like I killed this rabbit," I shouted in Donnelly's face, motioning with my head to the clean wet bones lying on the lawn near our bare feet.

Donnelly hated being backed down by a Mexican and a girl, especially when the girl was a Jew. But I could feel the rage of Jose, and Donnelly felt it too. He knew I would run him through if he came any closer. I pulled the arrow tighter against the string, noticing it was frayed, silently praying it would not snap. I waited for him to make a move while Clank stood frozen beside him. When Donnelly shuffled back a few inches, Clank repeated the motion. Then Donnelly took a full step back and Clank, of course, followed. As Sarah Jane and I moved forward, they slowly retreated from the lawn to the curb and back onto the street. I kept the arrow on Donnelly as he cautiously lifted his bike from the gutter, watching me closely. He mounted his bike, and Clank followed. As they began pedaling, I lifted the bow and shot an arrow straight up not knowing where it would land. Luck was strong then, and the arrow flew high before rocketing back down and barely missing Clank's back tire, bouncing off the pavement near him as he fell over onto the street.

They were soon up and racing away when Donnelly yelled, "Jew" to Sarah Jane. Then she let the rock fly and it whistled through the air, skipping over the tar road until it hit its mark low on Donnelly's back tire, which caused the wheel to wobble sending him to the ground again, hitting the street with a crash that could be heard throughout the neighborhood.

She picked up another rock from the flowerbed and walked toward him. Donnelly was looking up at her from the street as she held the rock in her cocked fist, staring down at the boy who now called for Clank's help. When Clank never came and she didn't move, Donnelly mounted his bike and caught up to Clank who was about a block ahead of him. When they were tiny in the distance, Donnelly yelled, "Jew girl," and then, "You'll be sorry, Mexican." I set an arrow against the string and lifted it to fire, but the string snapped and the arrow remained harmlessly in my hand.

"My name is Jesse, the son of Jose," I shouted, hoping Donnelly and Clank could hear me and never forget it. I kissed Sarah Jane on the lips. She smiled and giggled as I took her hand and pulled her down onto the grass where we traded kisses for hours.

When I finally went back into the house after dark, I looked out the front window watching Sarah Jane as she bounced home by the streetlights, safe from everything in the world. After that, I would see Sarah Jane every day and most nights that summer, often sneaking out of my parents' house late at night to sleep next to her in her tipi, but without having sex as Jose would have had wanted.

We didn't always hunt on the weekends. Sometimes we hitchhiked, sitting together on the curb between rides as I filled my dime store corncob pipe with discarded cigarette butts that we smoked. Together we visited all the great surfing beaches like Malibu and Rincon, but mostly Huntington Beach Pier since it was closest. All the guys liked Sarah Jane, and she had no trouble borrowing a surfboard. Nobody could believe I was her boyfriend.

She rode the biggest waves and did all the tricks like spinners and hanging five, sometimes even shooting the pier—riding through the dangerous cement pilings as the wave threatened to crush her—which it never did. Nothing could hurt Sara Jane. She tried teaching me surfing; but I never caught on, so she taught me to bodysurf. From then on, I bodysurfed in the shore break or played cards on the sand, smoking cigarettes and taking easy money from the local boys while she surfed.

One morning, Sarah Jane left the water happy and hungry, dried off, put on her T-shirt, and walked up to a tourist saying her father's car had run out of gas and asking for a nickel or a dime. The guy looked longingly at Sarah Jane, all wet and beautiful, and gave her a dollar. The next man she asked actually gave her five dollars before trying to kiss Sarah Jane. She slapped him hard but kept the money as she ran back to us. With six dollars, she treated our entire new Huntington crew—Curly, Smirk, Dave, Bones, and me-to pancakes at the Buzz Inn, across from the pier. It seemed that every day that summer Sarah Jane grew taller and prettier with her long, blonde hair turning silky white while her body grew into womanhood.

Sarah Jane was always looking to try something new, and sometimes we rode our bikes from Bell to East LA to see Jose who was back to his old self. He always cooked us good Mexican food and sat us down in the front room, asking if we were going to be married and have children. I turned red and silent, but Sarah Jane laughed, putting an arm around Jose, saying she wanted a man like him to marry. Then Jose stood and put his arm around her and kissed her on the cheek. "If you do not marry her, my idiot son, I will marry her for myself, this Sarah Jane, and then we will have many sons together and name the first one Jose and maybe even the second one also Jose, and the third one, and all of them will be Jose," he said, laughing hard. He was laughing and Sarah Jane thought he was kidding, but I knew better.

Jose had nearly forgotten about Soridtha who, without a word, walked into the kitchen where we were all seated. He quickly released Sarah Jane, saying he was joking, and his wife took him by the ear to sit on the couch in the front room while Sarah Jane averted her eyes.

Jose wanted one of us to have children with her, even though he was old and I was only fourteen and she was fifteen. Anyway, how could I have a son with her and then divorce her to become a priest? It was a foolish plan for many reasons, including the fact that priests cannot be married or divorced; but there was no use arguing with him about that.

Nobody who ever saw Sarah Jane could believe I was not in love with her. One night, alone with her in the tipi, I told her I did not love her as a wife. I kissed her as if she were my sister, and she kissed me as if she were my wife. I lay beside her, awake and holding her silently, until morning.

Maybe I didn't want to love Sarah Jane because nobody stayed in Los Angeles for long in those days and I expected she would soon be gone from my life, forever. It wasn't long before she and her family moved from California to Texas. I wrote to her once, putting my full name, Jesse Santiago Flannigan on the return address. When the letter came back to me unopened I was glad I never loved her.

# THE LONE RANGER RIDES AGAIN

*Al Nelson is among the most talented and least known surfer/designers of his time. A big-wave pioneer and a revolutionary board maker with Carl Ekstrom and Pat Curren, his feats are too numerous to list here. After I heard the following story from Carl Ekstrom, I thought "Pal Al" should apply to become a psychiatrist or a saint.*

–Originally published in *Kelea's Gift*

In over sixty years Alan Nelson has lived everywhere from Mainland China, where he was raised, to California, Hawaii, Costa Rica and Baja. He has mastered several languages, become a top-flight surfboard builder, an award-winning small plane designer, a big-wave pioneer, an ace trial attorney and a hard-living partner to Butch Van Artsdalen, Pat Curren and Bobby Patterson. Now, he was taking it easy, running a construction job in Cardiff, California, getting fine work done ahead of schedule and riding waves whenever possible. Living next door to the building site were a fifty-year-old man and his mother.

Al recognized the man as an independent thinker, and often went to him for advice, although the rest of the world had branded him autistic. Nobody but his mother had spoken to the boy for decades, and his brain had grown so brittle he rarely formed syllables any longer. That began to change when Al gave the man his own nail bag, hammer and construction hat, something he wore to the job, and put away each night at the foot of his bed in the wooden toy box with the *Lone Ranger* and Tonto painted on all four sides.

The man was up early each morning before the construction

crew arrived, watching the big trucks pull in with stacks of wood and bags of sand that were being magically transformed into a house. Every day at one o'clock, however, the man disappeared into his own house, to eat the deviled eggs and ham sandwiches his mother prepared for him and served on a cafeteria tray, leaving him alone to watch Lone Ranger reruns. He had seen every episode since his childhood, spending decade's worth of allowance on comics of the masked man. He also had a vast collection of posters, black masks and toy white horses, which covered every corner of his bedroom.

While he had never been so much as a minute late in the three months of his employment, one morning the man didn't show up for work at all. Thinking his friend might be ill, Al walked to the house at lunchtime and peered through the dusty screen door, straining to see Donald Duck flash across the old, wooden TV set. "Come in boss," said the man.

Al walked into the dark room, allowing his eyes to adjust as the man reclined on the sofa, still in his pajamas, with his lunch uneaten. He never turned to face Al, who took his place in a chair located in the corner of the room.

"Are you sick," asked Al.

"No," said the man, without diverting his attention from the TV set.

"Why weren't you at work today? We needed you."

Nothing was said, and Al and the man watched Donald Duck in an army uniform, making his usual mess of things, until one o'clock.

"Time for the *Lone Ranger*," said Al. Without turning his eyes away from the TV, the man spoke. "There is no Lone Ranger, boss. He's just an actor with a white horse. He isn't real."

"Who told you that?"

"He did," said the man, motioning with his head to a house four blocks down the street, where his only playmate, a boy of twelve lived. "No, he's just an actor." There was no joy or sadness in the man's voice, just the matter-of-fact dullness that often accompanies adult enlightenment. Al returned to work as the man sat, drinking Pepsi by the quart and watching cartoons, talk shows and televangelists. When Al returned that evening, the man was still seated alone, in front of the TV. This time, however, Al arrived with his favorite meal–cheeseburger, fries and chocolate malt. The man picked at the fries, and Al noticed a stack of Lone Ranger posters that had been taken from bedroom wall and were now piled up in front of the fireplace. The man looked into the TV set and repeated. "He's not real; just an actor."

An entire week passed and the man never came to the job or even left the house. His mother prepared food and then left for work, as her only son sat watching *Tom and Jerry*, *Lassie*, *M.A.S.H.*, *My Three Sons*, *All in The Family*, *Gomer Pyle USMC*, *Dragnet*, *Gilligan's Island*, *The Adventures of Scoobie Do*, everything but the *Lone Ranger*. Each day Al came by at lunchtime with food for himself and the man, who continued to recline listlessly in his pajamas, on the couch as Al sat nearby.

One day Al showed up with word from beyond. "I was over in the next valley," he said. The man was unmoved, watching *Green Acres*, barely smiling at the appearance of Arnold the Pig, quickly retreating to a blank expression after recalling what the boy had said, that it was a trick and the pig could not really talk. "In the valley I ran into a man on a white horse," Al continued. The man sat up and looked at the boss. Was he kidding? No, Al was serious as he continued. "He said the neighborhood was getting bad and he needs your help to clean it up." The man sat up straighter, straining to believe. But the proof given him by the boy had been strong, and was supported by the boy's mother and father who claimed to have seen the movie set where the *Lone Ranger* was filmed, in the hills near Hollywood. Then again Al had never lied to him. Confused by the contradictory evidence, the man collapsed hopelessly back onto the couch.

He returned to the TV screen as Al excused himself and made for the door. Suddenly Al stopped in the doorway and turned around, to face the man. "I almost forgot; he told me to give you something." Now, the man sat bolt upright, watching as Al took the shiny object from his pocket. A silver bullet! The TV did not exist as the man concentrated on the bullet that Al turned over to him. Clutching the bullet in his hand, the man looked up and said, "It's from him."

He turned off the TV, changed clothes and returned to the job. That evening the Lone Ranger was restored to his rightful place on his bedroom walls.

The next day the man showed up to work early and the rest of the crew were late, out having breakfast. Then the cement truck driver pulled up with a wet load of concrete. The man, who could easily pass for a construction foreman in his new overalls, pressed denim shirt and sport's cap, glared at the driver. He had seen the boss do this a million times. "Bring 'er on back," he shouted, waving the truck in. Thinking he was dealing with the foreman, the driver jerked the truck into reverse and headed back. The man never offered further instructions, and never flinched until the truck disappeared into the ravine and the driver bailed out on the dirt, screaming at the man, but unharmed.

When Al and the crew finally arrived on the job, the big truck was in the big ditch, on its side. Then came another big truck to haul the cement truck back onto the street. A TV reported had questioned the driver about the incident. Next, he interviewed the man, who said. "It's not my fault, the driver drove over the cliff. Over the cliff," he repeated, motioning to the downed cement truck. When the man spotted Al, he abandoned the TV crew and ran up shouting, "Boss, The Lone Ranger is real. He's real!"

Some time ago the man saved up his allowance to purchase a little glass case for the silver bullet. It remains on his nightstand to this day and is all the proof he'll ever need that someone is watching over him.

# THE EFFORTLESS PRUNE

*It was during a time of personal tragedy that a young Chris O'Rourke rescued me. He had yet to receive the plate in his head after a softball-sized piece of his skull had been removed, post brain surgery. Disregarding his own condition and showing concern for me, he drove to my house and took me home to stay with him and his little family. Moving his newborn son, Timmy into the bedroom with him and his wife Jill, he gave me use of their son's bedroom. For nights on end Chris sat up with me, listening and telling stories of his life. The following is one of those stories.*

–Originally published in *Good Thing Love Water*

By the time Chris O'Rourke had quit being afraid of the ocean he was twelve years old. That's when his older brother Bart, who had already been surfing for two years, dragged him down to La Jolla Shores and set him down next to his big surfboard in the wet sand. Bart had hoped Chris would become a good surfer, but little brother showed no promise of that whatsoever. He was a crybaby, complaining about the cold water and worried about being stung by a jellyfish. If Chris had his way, he would never enter the Pacific Ocean, but continue to comb the shore in pursuit of seashells.

Bart took a deep breath and tried to calm little brother. "Don't be a wimp; just try it once," he said. The boy remained unmoved by the taunt and didn't budge. Then, looking at his brother with unfelt contempt, he shook his head and said, "You'd never be Skip Frye anyway." With that Bart lifted the surfboard and prepared to return home. Chris glared at his brother angrily, wrenched the board from his arm, and with the victorious Bart close behind, entered the water.

115

Without any instructions, Bart pushed the kid out past the shorebreak, toward the gentle, little waves, where instinctively, awkwardly, the boy paddled toward the whitewater. He heard the voice of big brother, who was standing waist deep near shore, screaming for him to turn around and catch the next whitewater wave. Hoping to finish with surfing and resume his search for shells, Chris cooperated by getting off the board and spinning it around, until the nose faced shore. Then he laid flat on the board, paddled toward the beach, caught the whitewater and stood with his arms over his head, looking toward his stunned brother, laughing and shouting, "Skip Frye, Skip Frye," until the fin dragged on the sand and the boy fell down, face first. From then on Bart had trouble getting his board back. Chris had begun the long process of becoming a surfer.

These were lean times in the O'Rourke home, and there was no money for surfboards. Determined to surf, however, Chris scoured the beach near his home for Coke bottles, and cashed them in, making money on them and the fruit stolen from the neighbor's trees. After doing extra chores at home and cutting neighbor's lawns, he managed to save the necessary twenty-five dollars for a yellowed, delaminated Gordon and Smith Surfboard. The board, which was covered with dust and cobwebs, had been stored in a garage, unridden, for years. It had half a dozen unpatched dings, a cracked fin, and a faded picture of Jesus Christ emblazoned onto the deck. It was too old to surf well and too new to be an antique. It was a worthless piece of junk that Chris babied by removing the wax with hot water, before carefully sanding and polishing it with great care. Before re-waxing the board, he took a knife and carved all the wax from that filled the dings. He then cut into the foam, attempting to remove all the cancerous yellow spots. For the remainder of the day and long into the next, he mixed batches of resin, sometimes adding too much catalyst, and causing the mixture to catch fire. At other times he didn't add enough catalyst. This left the resin wet in places and brittle in others. Slowly, he patched the dings and the fin and sanded the board down until it was only slightly uglier than it had been two days earlier.

## The Effortless Prune

It was early April when Chris and his friend, Tim Bessell walked alone from their homes near Windansea to La Jolla Shores, two miles away. Neither of them admitted to it, but they took the walk in order to avoid the heavy reef breaks, and find a beach with gentle sand instead of sharp rocks.

Once at the Shores, they raced each other into the lineup where they competed in the surf, convinced in their minds they were ripping, unable to comprehend that they were not doing big, powerful turns, but merely tiny direction changes caused by trying to keep balanced. Yet each felt superior as he watched the other lumber gracelessly along in a foul squat. Still they hooted for one another, and were good enough friends to ignore each other's inflated remarks about their own surfing.

On the beach, a group of local kids in their early teens stood around a blazing fire with their shiny new boards and fashionable surf trunks. They were a little older than Chris and Tim and recognizable as some of the best young surfers in La Jolla. Chris walked forward and offered a friendly hello to the group. In return they eyed the ugly plank and the cutoff jeans, turned away and continued to talk and laugh among themselves, while occasionally glancing back at the new gremmie.

"Come on Chris, let's get something to eat," said Tim, in hopes of avoiding confrontation. With that Tim and Chris laid their boards near the firering and walked the half-mile to the market where they each bought a quart of chocolate milk and a dozen tiny sugar doughnuts.

On their way back to the beach they repeated familiar stories about their own great rides, catching the big waves that nobody ever saw, and swearing on their mother's graves that each fantasy tube and cutback were equal to any done by Skip Frye. It was a hot and glassy afternoon and they broke into a run in order to get back in the water quickly.

As they approached the beach, they heard laughter. Then they smelled burning plastic and noticed a black cloud forming on the horizon, spreading south with the wind. They saw the crew who had snubbed them earlier, standing around the fire ring, laughing and warming themselves on the flames. Chris and Tim laughed too, thinking that someone had thrown a tourist's beach chair into the fire again. But when Chris saw what was fueling the fire he yelled out, "My board! My board!" and ran over to save his beloved G&S from the flames. It was too late, however, as the entire nose and much of the stringer had been destroyed by fire. Of the fiberglass, little remained but glowing red and black charcoal. He burned his hands retrieving the remains of the board from the flames.

The crew howled with laughter as Chris put out the cinders of what had been his surfboard in the damp sand. Turning to the group, he yelled, "Who did this?" While most of them averted O'Rourke's penetrating eyes, the biggest of the crew marched forward. Puffing out his chest to capacity, he smiled and said, "I did it, kook!" Chris clenched his fist, and tagged the big kid on the jaw, as hard as he could, which really wasn't very hard. There was no pain and no blood from the weak punch, but the crew grabbed the aggressor and held him with their many arms.

A little shaken but still laughing at his wimpy attacker, the older boy did not strike back with fists, but said, "Split kook, you'd never be any good on that piece of shit anyway." Still restrained by the others, O'Rourke shouted back, "Within a year I'll out surf you all." He broke free and looked at each of them accusingly, and repeated, "I'll out surf all of you." They waited before he was out of earshot before they resumed laughing and talking.

Gathering what remained of his board, Chris walked to the water's edge, looking over his shoulder periodically so nobody could avoid his glare. Tim, who had also been restrained by the older kids, was now free, and walked over to comfort his friend. He turned away mercifully when he noticed Chris was sobbing. But the tears didn't last long. By the time he began the long walk home with the ruined surfboard, Chris was picking up any pop bottles he found in trash cans, holding each one like a first-place trophy before dropping it into the paper sack he had also retrieved from the trash.

Within a few days he had scrounged enough to buy a surfboard patch kit from Mitch's Surf Shop. He cut out the dead foam and then resined a new block of foam that he shaped with a file and sandpaper. He cut the cloth with his mother's scissors and poured resin from one of her aluminum pots. He would be punished for these infractions, but nothing could be worse than not surfing.

Mixing in the purple pigment with the intention of hiding the board's flaws, the dark color further emphasized his unskilled labor. The result of his artistry was that the board looked like a twisted and gnarled tree limb, painted purple. It was worse than that, really. The nose was thickly gobbed with resin and the purple blob was cracked in areas and permanently sand encrusted in others. When finished, Chris's older brother, Bart and his sister Lyn christened the board "The Effortless Prune."

Each day from then on, Chris walked to the Shores and surfed the disfigured Prune until after dark. He then walked back home alone, sometimes past his enemies who taunted him and mimicked his words, "Within a year I'll out surf all of you." Without replying, Chris would continue walking, pretending not to notice. Now he had a new, unseen purpose as the words boiled inside him, in a deep place where they festered and burned and hardened into determination.

By mid-June Chris was riding well in the greenwater. By July he could turn and cutback. By August he was better than average. By September he was better than most kids his age.

Each year at summer's end there was a surf contest for the kids at La Jolla Shores. Chris found the two-dollar entry fee in his sister's purse. For week's prior he practiced long and hard, sometimes surfing from dawn until dark. Each night he placed the Prune on his bed where he stood in bare feet, visualizing turns and cutbacks in order to simulate surfing. Before turning out the lights he would sit on the bed with the light on, going over and over the rules of the contest, eventually falling asleep clutching the paper and repeating things like, "Don't stand up after the horn."

A light fog hung over the water in the predawn hours as Chris paddled out alone to face the new swell and the rising sun. It was contest morning ,and he would rehearse everything again for the last time. Here he faced the small and glassy waves, making sure he had mastered every move he hoped to complete during the competition. On the beach he read the rules again. As the day progressed, kids gathered on shore, some of them paddling out before the event, while others simply stood around, confidently waiting for their heats to begin. All of the best gremmies in San Diego and some from as far north as Redondo Beach had gathered to compete in this contest.

O'Rourke drew an early heat, and he shook with cold and contest nerves as he placed the loose-fitting yellow jersey over bare skin. Padding out, he lost his board in the shorebreak before ever getting outside. He had no surf cord, and without looking to the beach, he swam in to retrieve the Prune. Eventually anger and determination overcame nerves, and he caught two of the biggest set waves and rode them without self-consciousness or excess, all the way to the sand. He caught three smaller waves also, falling only on the last one. Because of his extreme concentration on the event, he nearly stood up after the horn, something that would have disqualified him. He did not surf his best, but well enough to achieve third place in the heat, and advance to the next round. In his second heat, he had settled down a bit and pulled off a good cover-up, almost a tube. He took second that time and so continued to advance.

On his way up the beach, he passed the kid who had torched his surfboard. The kid had taken first in both his heats, while most of his crew had been eliminated early and were involved in ritual complaining about their boards, the waves, or the judging. When Chris walked directly past the kid and his crew and patted the Prune affectionately, nobody laughed.

An off-duty contest judge noticed the Prune and offered his own board, a perfectly crafted Caster swallowtail that Chris politely declined the use of. The Prune and its rider were inseparable now, as much a part of one another as salt is ocean water, and they stood out against the polish of the other boards and their riders. O'Rourke now became the main topic of the event, and some even attributed his success to his weird board.

In the finals, Chris didn't get any set waves or surf as good as he could have. Even if he had surfed his best he was not as good as the kid. On the winner's stand, the kid held his first trophy high, and gave Chris, who tightly clutched his fifth-place ribbon, a nod of acknowledgement.

Chris walked home carrying his two most prized possessions, the Effortless Prune and his ribbon. He intentionally took the long way as he headed for home, walking past the fire ring where the kid and some of his crew stood, admiring the first-place trophy. Looking over at O'Rourke as he passed them, someone shouted, "You kicked that kook's ass," in reference to the their friend's win. "I've got seven months to go before I beat you all," replied Chris, lifting his ribbon in a toast as he walked home.

*Chris O'Rourke, who was never again beaten by the kid, went on to be acknowledge as one of California's best surfers. He passed away in his early 20s after a bout with Hodgkin disease. His son Timmy and Timmy's mother, Jill, survive him.*

# THE HEART OF A MAN

–Originally published in *Kelea's Gift*

It was Tom who first met him on a diving trip to Pelelui where he had stayed with Robert Lewis Stevenson Camacho, and the entire Camacho family for three weeks. Tom decided to pay the family back for their generosity by bringing Robert back to our home in Guam. Never before had a member of the Camacho family been off their little island. Now, a seventeen-year-old boy named for the man who had written his father's favorite book, *Treasure Island,* had taken the big boat and the first step to what we like to call civilization. Pelelui was a full half-century behind the industrial revolutionized hum of America in the 1970s, and poor Robert Lewis had grown up without necessary items like Silly Putty, Hula Hoops, and plastic handled six-shooters.

When we met him at the dock he was silent, looking dreamily into the dirty water of the harbor. We realized later that he was afraid to speak or smile, embarrassed to reveal what a lifetime of chewing betel nut had done to his otherwise perfect Micronesian teeth. When Tom took him down the freight elevator, he clutched his arm like a child would a teddy bear, fearful that the floor was falling.

I got him a job as a gardener at the hotel where I worked as a waiter. Later, he was moved into a house the hotel kept for their employees. During that first month, he was so quiet we thought he knew no English. But soon he began speaking a quaint, easily understood form of Pidgin English used throughout Micronesia. Before long he was talking about everything, mostly his island home, and how he had speared big sharks and other fish. He talked about the way he and the other boys in his village had their eardrums broken by the older divers when they were children, so their ears would scar over and allow them to withstand the pressure of deep dives. Robert Lewis could freedive to seventy feet, something he was ashamed of, coming as he did from a place where good divers often topped ninety.

Still, he was the best diver known to us, disappearing far beyond the curtain of dark water, into the depths, often returning with fifty to eighty-five pound tuna thrashing to free themselves from the steel shaft of his homemade, wooden spear gun. After watching him, I wanted no part of my own store-bought metal gun, and asked him to make me one of like his. First we found a tree with good hardwood. Then, he cut down the tree and began whittling the wood into the shape of a musket. Next, he forged a metal can opener into a trigger, and ingeniously completed the process, using various pieces of junk, like an old bicycle inner tube. The thing looked like something out of the *Beverly Hillbillies,* but it shot straight, and I was able to land some big fish with it.

After a brief stint with homesickness, Camacho, as we called him, decided he liked the conveniences of Guam and would stay there for at least one year. With the exception of the hotel elevator, he was not afraid of anything. Not fire coral, sea snakes, sea wasps or the hammerhead sharks that swarmed as thick as Micronesian roaches in the water some days. He was a skilled fisherman, rarely missing the dime-sized kill spot of his prey, and always glad to share whatever he caught with the rest of us. He was a proud young man with only one black mark against him–no matter how he tried, he could never get deeper than seventy feet.

He trained in the hotel pool where I timed him swimming under water for up to two minutes. He sprinted on the beach, hyperventilating, and held his breath for four minutes at a time. He quit eating coconut crab, fruit bat and pork, and survived mainly on mangoes, rice and shark hearts, which he devoured raw while the shark's flesh was still quivering, before he took to cooking them whole on a stick over an open fire. He supplemented his diet with spoon meat coconuts, which he gathered daily by climbing the tall trees on the hotel grounds, shaking the trees back and forth, causing them to sway dramatically, before he jumped from one to the other. The Japanese tourists at the hotel loved the act, and he was soon hired by the management to perform near the pool each evening in a grass skirt. After descending from thirty or forty feet, he would open the coconuts with a machete and bring them to the tourists who drank from them while Camacho danced to a conga drum and sang in his native tongue. With the extra money he made, he consulted a witchdoctor and paid a vast sum to the woman who said she could help him dive deeper than any man alive. He was hopeful until she was arrested for fraud. Nothing helped. He was doomed to diving no deeper than seventy feet.

"I want you to take me to America, Crees. I have been watching the television, and I have found out there is a place called Medical Center. You will bring me there, and they will operate on me to give me a turtle heart," he said, one morning.

"Camacho, Medical Center is only a TV show, and nobody can give you a turtle heart," I said to him.

"No, I must go to Medical Center and get a turtle heart, even if you do not help me to do it."

We argued about Medical Center and the turtle heart until I realized I was getting nowhere with him. Finally I asked, "Camacho, why do you want a turtle heart?"

"You think I am only a stupid island boy, but I have thought on this for a long time. Think about what I am saying, Crees. I cannot get an eel heart because it is too small. A tuna heart would cause me to be fast, but not so brave. I thought maybe a shark heart. That would make me brave and fast, but mean, like the shark, and then I would be in trouble from always biting people and maybe even biting Kojak when I am in America, and then Kojak would hunt me down and kill me. A turtle heart, you see, will make me strong and fast and brave and still nice, and I could dive more than one hundred feet. Please, I never ask you for anything, Crees. Please, go with me to Medical Center for the turtle heart."

Nothing I said dissuaded him, and so I flatly stated that I would not accompany him to America. He threw his knife angrily between my feet, before picking it up and walking away. After that he avoided me for a while and tried to find other Americans to take him to Medical Center for the new heart.

He came to me one day with a gift of betle nut and lime and a six-pack of beer, and we were soon seated on the beach, drinking, talking and laughing. Slowly, he came to the point of his visit. He had seen surfing and he wanted to try it. The next day I took him to a learner's spot, a mushy, rolling wave. He took one look at the Waiki-ki-type surf, shook his head, and said, "No Crees, this is not surfing. This is playing like the children in the hotel pool with toys. I want to ride in the tube. Take me to a place where I can ride in the tube." I told him it was not safe to ride the tube over coral on your first day. "Ah, Crees, you are disappointing me once again," he said.

There are tubular places like the ones Camacho wanted to ride on Guam, but they are crowded and have nasty bottoms, covered with sharp coral. Then again Camacho was young, brave and as coordinated as a spider monkey. Against my better judgment, I took him out to a mini Pipeline with a savage bottom. I decided to paddle out with him, and put him well onto the shoulder, where I would push him into the smaller waves. Since most beginners think they are in the tube most of the time anyway, my plan was to let him catch a few waves on the edge, and tell him he was in the tube.

Upon our arrival at the tube spot I noted a dozen others out, all decent surfers, good enough to get in the tube occasionally, something Camacho desperately wanted to try. He was so excited he wore his trunks in the car, and while I changed in the public restroom, he took my board from the roof, and began paddling out. I called to him from shore, but if he heard me he didn't turn around. I paddled out on the board I had brought for him, and entered the lineup right as he was finding his way into the middle of the pack.

The sets were a solid six feet, top to bottom and spitting into the channel. Every longtime surfer on Guam had major coral cuts and even the most experienced of them dreaded going over the falls there. Someone caught a wave, got barreled and spat out onto the shoulder. There he fell, hit bottom and came up bleeding from the forehead. The surfer was shaken as he paddled in. I figured that would scare Camacho out of trying these waves, but he persisted, undaunted. I paddled into the pack to rescue him, but he avoided me and paddled to the inside. There, he paddled for a smaller wave and I watched helplessly as the strong offshore wind pushed him over the top, before he could drop in. I caught the next wave and rode to the inside. I was paddling out in the channel when I saw him in position, stroking hard for the wave he wanted. He missed that one too, and it exploded on the inside reef.

I was seated next to him, yelling at him dodging the sets and trying to get him to listen to me and paddle onto the shoulder. "No Crees; that is not where the tube is. If you want to play like a child, riding baby waves, go ahead, but I must have the tube." He paddled back into the pack where he earned respect from the others, mostly sons of soldiers whose fathers had been stationed there. Nobody said a word as he paddled for the next wave, his shiny brown skin tightening as he stroked into a beautiful six-foot peak.

Camacho paddled as if he had the heart of a great white shark beating in his chest. He paddled like all great surfers paddle, with commitment and power, lacking only technical skill, which caused him to move like a wounded fish, the type in danger of being eaten by predators. He continued paddling as the wave stood tall behind him. I had never seen anyone catch a green water wave their first time out, but here was Camacho, coming together with the tube of his dreams.

Somehow, he made the drop, got to one knee, got in the tube for a split second and went over the falls. From behind I could see his body roll over a second time, and prayed he would not hit bottom. Long seconds passed and I paddled to the inside to find him. There were stories of surfers getting caught in underwater caves here, and the longer I paddled the more worried I became, wondering if I was going to break his parent's hearts by telling them their son had drowned while I was teaching him to surf. I heard him before I saw him, laughing and shouting, " I love the tube, Crees. I love the tube."

I expected him to return to the lineup, but Camacho paddled into shore, satisfied. He never surfed or spoke about surfing again, saying as he dried off that day, "Surfing is nice, but it is only too easy. Already in one day I can ride the tube better than you, and it is enough for me. I do not want to keep riding the tube again and again, and maybe missing a lot of good days of fishing and working just so that I can go into the tube all of the time."

On our next day off, we drove to the far end of the island to a spot where we had been driving once before. While changing into our trunks, Camacho told me of a crazy man who lived nearby, and once took a shot at him. Months later, I read in the papers about Sargent Yokoi, the Japanese soldier, who had been left on Guam like an unexploded mine. Yokoi had heard the war was over, but believed it to be Yankee propaganda. After his capture, he was taken home to Tokyo where he lived the life of a confused patriot, watching his people pledge their allegiance to tall, American-inspired buildings and new technology.

The diving was bad that day and for many more days in a row. Camacho was bored when he decided to visit his cousins in the Philippine Islands for a month. He was such a good and hard worker that the hotel gave him leave with half pay and the promise he would get his job back when he returned. Upon his return he did not talk about diving or surfing or turtle hearts, but about the poor people in the Philippines and how many were finding poverty and drugs. "Even one time a man tried to get me to put a needle in my arm for drugs. When I said that I would never do that, he became angry with me, Crees. I hit him in the face, but he still tried to make me put the drugs in my arm. When he would not leave me alone, I told the police. Now this man is on Guam with his family. I saw him today, Crees, and he told me he knows where I live and that he will come there at dark, only to kill me."

That night I took a baseball bat from the hotel and followed Camacho to his home. He lived in a wooden shack with a Micronesian couple and their four children. We cooked the large fish Camacho had speared a few days prior over a homemade fire ring. Micronesians are generally friendly, festive people, but on this night they exhibited nothing but fear. The muddy road offered one way in and one way out. The shack was boarded up, and one at a time the residents kept watch from high atop a coconut tree. The children alone were without fear, making a game of standing watch. Unable to climb the coconut tree myself, I did my duty, sitting up in a wooden chair inside the house, clutching the baseball bat, praying I would not have to use it.

Morning was a gift to us all, and joy returned to the shack as everyone ran out to pick wild fruits wet from the night rain in the jungle as Camacho and I drove off to work, laughing and talking. "You are a good friend to me, Crees. You have risked yourself for the life of me and of my friends. But if you have done such a thing for me, why then will you not go with me to America and to Medical Center for the turtle heart that I must have. You yourself are not such a good diver, and you should have a turtle heart for yourself. Since you have saved me, I will pay for your own heart, as a gift from me to you, Crees. Come, let us go to America. It is not so far away."

# CAPTAIN
# COURAGEOUS

*In the mid 1960s Paul Strauch was ranked among the best surfers in the world. Those who saw him in his prime, including Greg Noll, Jeff Hakman and Gerry Lopez claim he was the best ever. He is also a humble, humorous individual, traits he learned from his mentor, Duke Kahanamoku. When he tells this tale of the Duke, you feel like you're in the boat with them.*

–Originally published in *Kelea's Gift*

As a member of the prestigious Duke Kahanamoku Surf Team along with Fred Hemmings, Butch Van Artsdalen and Joey Cabell, Paul's job was to keep the Duke from dozing off during press conferences. During his many interviews Duke wore dark sunglasses to camouflage his napping habit, which he often did at press time. One tap on the knee from Paul would wake the legendary waterman, and he would answer, "Yes," to the question. Two taps on the knee brought the answer, "No." Naps were not confined to land, however, and while working as a diver in Honolulu Harbor, the father of modern surfing would curl up near the keel of some boat and snooze until he needed to surface for air. His relaxed manner carried over to everything he did, especially fun, which he always loved having.

Disneyland had recently opened and Duke wanted to be among the first on the rides. He loved the Jungle Boat ride best, where wild animals appeared along the river and the captain fired at them with his pistol. The little boat was moving down the river, and the brave captain did his duty to protect all passengers by shooting at the hippos and crocodiles that threatened safe passage. A wide-eyed

*Duke looked at him, saying,*
*"You'd better hang on; this ride's gonna get rough."*

young boy seated near Duke was taking the trip for the first time. Duke looked at him, saying, "You'd better hang on; this ride's gonna get rough." The boy held tightly to the rail as the boat hit rapids and was tossed around violently. True to his lifelong habit Duke wasted no time rescuing those in need. He stood up and took hold of the tiller of the boat and began steering, much as he had done for years in outriggers off Waikiki. He was jerked from side to side as the boat teetered on the edge of disaster. The little boy looked with admiration to Duke, who was hard at work keeping the vessel from going over. The Hawaiian's majestic white hair was flying as he held tightly to the tiller and the little boy hugged his seat tighter.

Suddenly the rapids subsided and the boat was moving through calm water again. The captain tied up to the dock, and the little boy approached Duke to thank him for saving him and his entire family. "It's a good thing you listened to me," said Duke, putting a gentle hand on the boy's shoulder. "You gotta be prepared when things get rough." Only years of water time could teach him that.

# GREENHORN IS COWBOY FOR KOOK

*More than a decade before the movie* City Slickers, *my brother, Dave and I ventured off to become cowboys. The resulting culture clash was as abrupt as if we had met cattle ranchers from outer space.*

–Originally published in *Good Things Love Water*

By the summer of 1967 I had been surfing for five years. While I loved riding waves, it had become repetitive, and I longed for something new. I was eighteen-years-old and my shoulder-length hair and Indian beads hid the cowboy within. We lived a hundred years and a thousand miles beyond cattle country, near East Los Angeles, just a few miles from the Sunset Strip where I hung out on weekends.

While most of my surfer friends had become hippies and burned with Jimi Hendrix and Janice Joplin, my aching heart rode sidesaddle with Hank Williams. I worshiped John Wayne and had nearly memorized every one of the lines from his movies. As a closet cowboy, I often hid *Rodeo Magazine*, a magazine that changed my life, within the covers of the *LA Free Press*.

Miraculously the ad jumped from one of its back pages: Experienced Cowhands wanted. Send Qualifications to Donald Fredricks, Triple-D Ranch, Horse Mountain, Nevada.

I sent Fredricks a letter that day–told him that my brother and I had grown up riding and breaking horses, on the family ranch. Actually, we had merely rented a few broken down mares at Griffith Park a few times, and while we had ridden well, nothing could justify the fantasy of being real cowboys. My hands shook as I read his return letter a few weeks later:

Dear Mister Ahrens, Thank you for your kind correspondence. Should you and your brother accept my offer, you can begin work immediately. Pay, including room and board is $90.00 a month.
Sincerely,
Donald Fredericks,
Triple-D Ranch,
Horse Mountain, Nevada

Dropping the letter to the floor I let out a loud whoop, and prepared to ride the range.

After exaggerating our wages to Dave, I convinced him to join me, saying it was a good way to earn money for the coming winter, in Hawaii. We did odd jobs, sold an extra surfboard, bought cowboy hats, boots and a couple tins of *Redman Chewing Tobacco*. Within a week we were driving east to Nevada.

For the first time in my life I felt free to switch the radio station from rock to country, turned it up good and loud and packed my cheek with a chaw. Then I floored it for Tonopah in my 327 1955 Chevy that I hoped to trade for a horse, a saddle and a pickup truck.

In Tonopah my California plates attracted a lot of attention, especially from teenaged girls. A cute hippie girl in an Indian blouse and hip huggers eyed the car and slinked over to introduce herself.

"Hi, I'm Phyllis," she said. After we introduced ourselves she asked if we wanted to come to a party.

"We can't," I said. "We're on our way to the town of Horse Mountain."

"It's no town; it's just a mountain," she said, laughing. The other girls giggled, but kept their distance. Phyllis was doing the talking. "What are you doing here anyway? This place is dead," said Phyllis. She spat out her gum, lit a cigarette and blew the smoke into the bright blue air.

"We're on our way to the Triple-D Ranch; you know where it is?"

"The 3-D? Yeah, I know. Just follow 8-A west, and look for

the sign by the road."

"How far is it?"

" 'Bout eighty miles."

"What's the next town?"

"No town between here and Horse Mountain, just tumble-weeds and cow shit," she said, while turning her attention from me, onto Dave. Then, in a convincing display of hurt feelings, she said, "You sure you don't want to come to my party?"

"We'll party with you next weekend," said Dave with a smile.

"Okay, I'll see you both next weekend," she said in a sexy voice. After scribbling her name and number on the back of a match-book, she threw it into Dave's lap and slinked slowly away.

It was long after dark when we roared into the 3-D, which is what we were calling it now. A towering, square-framed man with a 55-gallon drum of a hat practiced lassoing fence posts beneath a naked light bulb in an otherwise empty corral. As we broke dust and silence, he faced us and watched as the frantic Chevy approached. He stood straight and silent with one hand on his hip, as if we were in a showdown together. He didn't budge as I parked and made my way toward him, talking fast and extending my hand while still a horse's tail away. "Hi, you the foreman? You Mister Fredericks?" I asked.

"Nope," he replied slowly, before spitting in the dust, straight-ening the big hat and looking down at me. "I'm just one of the buck-aroos." My hand still extended, I nearly swallowed the chaw in my mouth, but somehow kept from laughing. Dave, who always laughed at the wrong time, doubled over and walked back to the car where he fell into a fit of laughter that could be heard all the way to the corral. We had only heard words like buckaroo spoken in old Gabby Hayes movies. I struggled to keep control, but Dave's distant howls caused me to laugh right in the big man's face.

Without moving or saying a word, the buckaroo wiped my spray from his face with the bandana he kept in his back pocket. "Sorry," I said. "We've been on the road too long." The buckaroo nev-er changed expression, and I was sure he didn't buy my lame excuse.

Again, I put my hand forward, saying, "My name's Chris."

Crushing my hand and looking me dead in the eye he said in a deep voice, "Name's Stumpy." Dave overheard the name and began laughing louder. Still within Stumpy's grasp, I laughed in his face again. His eyes narrowed like Clint Eastwood ready to gun someone down. He yanked his big hand away, wiped his face with his bandana again and growled, "Follow me," before stomping away on the hard dirt.

I followed Stumpy on foot, threw the car keys to Dave, and told him to tail us in the car. The bunkhouse was a stark rectangular wooden box filled with the sounds of loudly snoring men. Without a word, Stumpy threw us a couple of blanket and left. We bedded down in a corner of the bunkhouse, as far from the other bucka-roos as possible. It was still dark when I was awoken by something poking me in the ribs, followed by a deep voice saying, "Get up, get dressed and follow me." It was Stumpy, who, like most everyone on the ranch, woke before sunrise.

Dave took a swing at me when I shook him awake, but I yanked him from his bunk, still dressed in his clothes from the night before. He shuffled along tiredly behind us as I tried making friendly conversation with Stumpy, who kept several paces ahead of me. He didn't react to anything I said, but kept walking while looking at the ground. When he finally did speak, his words weren't directed at me or anyone else. "Fredericks is the owner of the Triple-D, but he ain't no cattleman–the idiot's a banker from Hollywood who thinks it's fun raisin' beef. He don't raise beef, I do." He spat a gob of tobacco juice onto the ground to punctuate the statement.

Parked next to the bronzed horse hitch was a big, four-wheel drive truck with cowhide seat covers and the flaming Triple-D brand delicately airbrushed onto both doors along with celestial cowboys chasing cattle through the clouds. I followed Stumpy into a big Vic-torian style two-story house and walked the oak stairway to Mister Fredericks' office. Stumpy knocked, and moments later the man I would come to know as Donald Fredericks answered.

Fredericks looked more like Barney Fife than John Wayne. He was a withered man–about five-four without his high healed cowboy boots, with thinning black dyed hair and a matching mousy moustache. He led the fashion roundup in designer jeans, a silky black cowboy shirt, matching bandana around his neck, gray lizard boots and a small, delicate cowboy hat tilted to one side of his head. Chopin mixed awkwardly with moose and buffalo heads, Remington copies, and Greek sculpture. There was no Misses Fredericks.

Fredericks smiled like Cal Worthington winding up to deliver an entire herd of Dodge vans. "Welcome gents, you must be the Ahrens boys," he said, holding out his hand to shake.

"Yes sir," I replied, enthusiastically. "I'm Chris and this is Dave." Fredericks asked us to be seated, and motioned us to a deerskin covered couch. "Herb tea, gents?" he asked, holding up a steaming teapot bearing the Triple-D brand. We took our tea, but Stumpy passed and rolled his eyes, beyond Fredericks' line of sight.

Fredericks explained how he had built the place up from nothing to one of the biggest herds in Nevada while Stumpy wrung his hands tightly and gazed at the floor. After a brief history of his life, Fredericks smiled, winked and patted my leg. "You won't need to break any horses for a while," he said as I pulled my leg away. Fredericks continued, "You'll mend fences and go on the occasional cattle drive. Stumpy here will be your boss, and he'll cut out horses for you when you need 'em." Stumpy smiled sadistically, we shook hands all around and left the house.

After a breakfast of ham and eggs at headquarters, Stumpy walked us over to a corral filled with fat, lazy cows and said, "I don't care what that bastard said, no greenhorns are ridin' my horses. You boys are gonna herd cattle all right–on foot!"

Stumpy walked us to a stall filled with cows where two men were slogging through a mixture of muddy shit trying to get the fattened animals to move. "This is Hank," said Stumpy. "He'll be your supervisor." Without another word, Stumpy walked off to saddle up, and moments later we watched as he and several other cowboys rode off into the sunrise. Hank shrugged his shoulders in recognition of our horseless fate, but his partner, Dennis, gave an admiring look at the cowboys as they rode off. "Sure wish I could go with 'em," said Dennis, like a kid making a request to Santa Claus.

Hank was a short, nervous nail biter of about thirty with spiky brown hair extending for a month-old crew cut. "Green Giant" in Idaho had fired him for rustling vegetables. Turns out, he had answered the same advertisement we had in *Rodeo*. While hitchhiking to the ranch he teamed up with Dennis, a tall, skinny, flabby-hearted bookkeeper from Chicago.

Dennis kept asking us for pictures and phone numbers of girls we knew. Worn out by his repeated pleading, I produced a wallet photo of Poly, my part-time ex-girlfriend from home. Her phone number was written over the photo. Dennis looked for a moment, and handed the photo back without comment.

Later, Dennis told me Poly was a bitch. Amazed by how much he had learned from a single photo, I congratulated him on his gift of discernment. Only when I returned to Hollywood did I discover that he had called Poly, and proposed marriage that day. Thinking it was me disguising my voice, she said yes to the proposal and went along with the joke for a while. When she realized it was a stranger on the line and that he was serious, she slammed down the receiver. Dennis, who had memorized her phone number, called back five more times, and each time Poly hung up on him.

Dennis sobbed as he told me about another heartbreak. He was on his way to Los Angeles from Chicago to marry a girl whom he had spoken to only once over the phone. That's when his car broke down in Tonopah, he met Hank and they hitchhiked to the ranch.

Hank didn't care much for ranch life, but Dennis loved it so much he left his long-distance bride at the altar. He didn't contact her until two weeks after the arranged wedding date, asking if she wanted to be a cowboy's wife. He claimed he was a ruined man ever since she changed her phone number.

Dennis was also a library of hopefully inaccurate information about everybody on the ranch. After cluing us into the quirks of each ranch hand, he paused and asked, "You guys met Sam yet?"

"No," I replied.

"Well, stay away from him. He shot and killed a man and buried him on the range, not far from here. He hates hippies like you, and he's real mean. Once he had me herd a corral of bulls. He told me they were cows, and nearly got me trampled to death." Dave and I laughed, but in reality we were terrified of meeting Sam.

After shoving cows around until dark, Hank and Dennis showed us to the TV room, where Dave and I sank down into a dusty sofa. Hank's eyes grew wide as we sat down. "Don't sit there; that's for buckaroos only," he shouted. Hank and Dennis didn't see anything funny, but we were laughing so hard they began laughing also.

As we sat laughing, Stumpy and the man I would soon know as Sam led the other cowhands into the room. They seemed stunned by our trespass. Dave continued laughing, stood up, and held out his hand to shake with Sam, who slapped it away violently. We simultaneously noticed Sam's six-shooter, a dark piece of metal protruding from a worn leather holster. I began thinking that Dennis might have told the truth about Sam murdering a man. Quietly defeated, Dave and I returned to the wooden benches where we sat with the other greenhorns while the cowboys made under-the-breath remarks about us.

Dave and I took our abuse silently, but Dennis boldly asked to borrow a smoke from Sam, of all people. Sam shook the pack and a couple cigarettes popped out the top. He held them out to Dennis, who started over to get one when he was tripped by one of the boys. Everybody laughed except we four greenhorns. Even Dennis laughed a little, in a slightly humiliated way that he seemed familiar with. But he dusted himself off and continued walking to get his smoke.

Sam grinned at me through his broken yellowed and gold-capped teeth, silently daring me to say something. Dennis's warning about Sam kept me in check. I looked away as Sam laughed meanly.

Dennis was tripped again on his return to the bench, but he held his lit cigarette up like a trophy, proud that it hadn't broken. Then he sat down and watched *"The Monkees"* with the cowboys and us.

Sam whispered something to Stumpy. The two men laughed as Sam nodded to Dennis and asked, "You wanna join us in the branding tomorrow?"

"Sure do," replied Dennis, brightly.

"Be ready to ride at dawn," said Sam. Without another word, Dennis bolted from the room.

I didn't see him again until late that night when he woke me by turning on the light over my bunk. "Well, how do I look?" he asked. With his shiny black hat, cheap Naugahyde chaps and tinny spurs attached to his patent-leather boots, he looked like Captain Kangaroo dressed up to play Jesse James. He looked like a book-keeper, about to go trick-or-treating. He stood proudly at the foot of my bunk, drew a pretend six-shooter with his finger and said, "Draw partner."

"You look like Billy The Kid," I said. "Now turn off the light and go to sleep."

He shot his finger at me again, and said, "Yeah I do look like a buckaroo, don't I?" He finally switched off the light, but woke nearly every hour to check the time and spit on his new boots.

That morning after breakfast, Dave and I dragged over to mend fences while Dennis bounced past us on his way to ride the range. I was jealous at first, but after a few hard falls trying to mount his horse, I felt sorry for him. When he was finally seated on the horse, he looked our way, waved his hat and yelled, "Giddy up!" The horse stood still. Kicking and swearing, Dennis had no luck moving the beast until suddenly it reared up, took off and flew past us and the other cowboys. The last we saw of Dennis that morning he was galloping deep into the prairie, somehow hanging on while the men shouted mock encouragement at him.

By mid-day, roughly 100 calves had been branded and herd-ed into the corral near our work area. Dennis rode in a full hour after the others. His clothes were filthy, his chaps scuffed, and he had a big lump on his forehead. But he smiled, sat up straight in the saddle and gave us "thumbs up" as he rode past.

Being kind of proud of Dennis we returned the gesture, but the cowboys made crude fun of him. These were nothing like the men I had seen in *The War Wagon* or *High Noon*. They were petty men, not worthy of shinning Shane's belt buckle.

Still, there was something great about them when they rode from the saddle. I watched Stumpy turn his cutting horse perfectly into the herd, pick out a calf, work it to the edge, toss his rope around its hind legs and pull it to the flankers for branding. He rode tall and was quick, powerful and commanding with a delicate touch when necessary. For that one moment he was my hero. He transformed quickly as he climbed down from his horse, looked at me and asked, "What are you lookin' at, greenhorn?"

We had been at the 3-D for three weeks, and Dave and I were still herding cattle on foot. We worked sunup to sundown, six and a half days a week. One day after work I was so tired I fell asleep on the couch reserved for the buckaroos. I woke suddenly with something poking me in the ribs. Pushing the blunt object away, I woke to see Sam prodding me with his pistol. "Move or die," he growled. I sat and moved across the room.

The other cowboys made their usual mean remarks as they passed. Dennis, who now rode with them regularly, walked in behind them. He stomped past us without eye contact. His thumbs were tucked beneath his belt as he marched to the couch and sat down between Sam and Stumpy, like they were old friends.

"Hey Dennis, how'd it go today?" asked Hank sincerely. Dennis struck a match on the sole of his boot, lit a smoke, took a deep drag, exhaled and glanced coldly at the three of us. "You greenhorns probably think it's fun ridin' the range, don't you?" he said. Even Dave was too stunned to laugh. Dennis had deserted us and joined the buckaroos.

Two days later, just before chow, Dave led Hank and me to

the bunkhouse refrigerator. There, he pulled out a long, plump rainbow trout and held it by the gillplate with his index finger. He told us about a little cement pond nearby that was packed with fish. He had made a hook from a straight pin, tied a piece of cotton string to it, baited it with roast beef and pulled in the fish within seconds. We fried the trout on the bunkhouse hotplate with the potatoes that Hank had rustled from headquarters. After dinner we threw the remains of our feast into the trash.

It was dark when Hank and I followed Dave to the pond. Before we arrived, we saw Sam with a big net, hauling in fish and putting them into a sack. We watched from a safe distance as he filled two more sacks, put them into his truck and drove off, no doubt to sell them in town. Sam must have taken all the fish, because we didn't catch anything that night.

It was a few days before Hank told us that Fredericks was mad as hell, and had ordered a meeting of all hands after morning chow.

"If he's mad, it means the cleaners went on strike," said Dave in reference to of the immaculate outfits the man wore. We laughed, but I figured we were headed for trouble.

Donald Fredericks sat resplendent in his matching red Sunday outfit at the head of the big table. Trying to make his tinny voice sound tough, he began. "Men," he said, "it has come to my attention that somebody's been fishin'." Pausing for effect, he raised his voice, looked directly at me and added, "My private breeding pond has been completely fished out!"

He pounded the wooden table with just enough restraint to keep his puny fist from being injured. Fredericks took a deep breath and paused to calm himself. He was sweating and hyperventilating. Fred, the cook, slapped him on the back to keep him breathing. Nobody else dared speak, but the boys threw occasional fierce glances at Dave and me. They figured we'd done it for sure. Luckily, Dave looked away from the comical sight of Fredericks' tomato-red face. If Dave looked over for even a second, he would explode in laughter and the cowboys would finish us off, right there.

Fredericks drew a deep breath, and continued. "Now, I'm not accusing anybody, but I expect the guilty party to come forward and see me privately. I won't press charges, but I will doc the man's pay accordingly. I think that's more than fair." Doing the math in my head I figured we would be working for free for six months if we were convicted of being the guilty party.

Dave and I walked quietly out the back door to avoid confrontation. Being Sunday, we only worked half day. We skipped lunch and drove to the local bar a few miles up the road where we played pool, had a few beers and discussed our escape plans. Nobody would believe Sam had taken all the fish. Even if they did, it would be suicide to tell Fredericks, since he valued Sam far more than any of the other ranch hands, especially us. With no other options, we decided to sneak out in the morning. Fredericks could keep the few dollars he owed us.

We stopped at the bunkhouse to gather our belongings, and found Dennis sitting on his bunk shinning his boots when we arrived. We didn't tell him we were leaving, but Dave stuck out his hand and shook with him, saying we wanted to be friends again. To assure good intentions, Dave handed Dennis the matchbook with Phyllis' number on it, the girl we had met in Tonopah on our way to the 3-D. Dennis took the number, smiled broadly, thanked Dave and shook hands, first with him, then with me.

After sleeping lightly that night, we woke an hour before dawn, packed our car and filled the tank from the ranch gas pump. Fredericks owed us at least that much.

We peeled out for headquarters where I spun doughnuts in the dust, and blasted my horn. First Fredericks, then Sam came running out to meet us, and Sam foolishly charged the car as I swerved to miss him. In his frenzy Fredericks ran toward the car and slung a little rock from his shoulder; in the way one would throw a shot put. The pebble bounced off the window, and we laughed until we remembered Sam was armed and probably dangerous. I put the throttle to the floor and sprayed Fredericks with his own dirt and gravel. When the dust cleared, we could see him raising his fist, screaming and jumping up and down. Monday's white outfit was filthy.

My wheels bit into the dust a little as we burned out for the main gate, hoping it would be open. Stumpy, who had just woken to the ruckus, was tucking in his shirt as he jumped behind the wheel of Frederick's truck as Fredericks and Sam piled in next to him. Thankfully the gate was open, and we pulled onto the main highway with the cowboys close behind.

Fredericks' truck was fast, and they were on our tail for a few miles. From my rearview mirror I could see Fredericks jumping around in his seat like a furious squirrel. Dave turned around and exploded with laughter when he saw Fredericks leaning out the window, shaking his fist. When Sam leaned out beyond Fredericks and pointed his six-shooter out the window at us, I put the pedal down and they disappeared in the distance. Stumpy slowed the truck and pulled over to the side of the road. No shot was ever fired, and I believe that Stumpy had restrained Sam from firing at us.

The power of the 327 ate up the road as the 3-D Ranch and its workers faded forever into the distance. We didn't slow down until Tonopah. There, cruising slowly down the main street, I caught sight of a tall, thin man dressed in white bell-bottoms, a paisley shirt and a beaded Indian headband. In one night Dennis had gone from cowboy to hippie. We couldn't stop to talk, but honked and waved. With one hand he flashed the peace sign. With the other he held onto Phyllis.

# THE BIRTHDAY PARTY

–Originally published in *Joyrides*

Joe Watterson sat up, rested his flabby thighs on the edge of his bed and thought long and hard about his pathetic life. He remembered many things from his past–women, parties, and honors bestowed by his company. His mind touched down on the pleasant days of his youth, and he was filled with images of beautiful surfboards, wild characters, and mountains of surf. He inched his way up out of bed to a peak of joy. Then, he roller coastered down, into a pit of bottomless despair.

The reason for this morning's reflection was his coming birthday. Tomorrow he would be forty-five years old. There was nothing to celebrate other than survival, and nothing to be proud of since the age of fourteen, when he had been one of Waikiki's hottest kids. That childhood seemed to belong to someone else now. He had only surfed a few times in the past decade, and not once in the last year–not since Mindy, his wife of eighteen years had packed up the kids and left for her mother's home in Detroit.

He had no more feeling about his current life than if he had been frozen solid in a distant ice age. He did nothing but work and grow old and fat and stupid in the safe claustrophobia of his tiny apartment. When by degrees his brain overheated, he was dangerous.

He watched little people act out heir little lives for the approval of Oprah and Phil, and he contemplated his own tiny existence while living vicariously through idiots. He shouted at their stupidity and cheered their victories. "The invisible people," he secretly called them as he watched them disappear each time he switched off the TV set. Watterson himself felt like one of the invisible people. He lit a big bowl of his favorite medicine and evaporated into the walls.

How long had he existed in this hazy world, feeling he could almost pass through walls? But the more he hated his life, the deeper it sucked him in, down into that feeling, if it could be called a feeling, that was as much like nothingness as something could be.

Each day the thin walls absorbed muffled cries from the ghosts of his wife and children, and his old surfing buddies, some who had died from distilled causes. There were holes in the walls where he had tried punching his way out of the feeling.

It had not gone well yesterday at the insurance office where he worked. He made no sales and came home early, just in time to pound four tall beers and slam two shots of tequila. In the old days he drank to feel good; now he drank to feel nothing.

He rolled from the bedroom onto the couch and listened as an invisible woman read an invisible poem about her invisible cat on the invisible news station. In former rages he had broken just about everything in the house. Pottery, picture frames, dishes and cheap furniture all lay in a heap, right where he had smashed them. Now he kicked his last true companion, the nineteen inch TV. He kicked it again, and the glass shattered the woman's face. To Joe's pleasure the cat woman faded in and out of focus. He kicked again and again, until the woman vanished from his sight, leaving sparks and smoke where her face had been. Only grayness and her shrill voice were left now. When he delivered the deathblow, the sound mercifully failed. Having destroyed the foundation of his life he went back to bed without removing he clothes.

He had not slept this well since he was a gremmie, surfing Baby Queens'. He stayed in bed and soaked up the peace of the rainy morning. Fading and out, he half dreamed of his youth and of surfing big waves, something he had never really done. For the first time in recent memory, he awoke smiling.

He rose, fixed bacon and eggs and, instead of reporting to the office, went to the bank. There he withdrew the remaining $1,434.24 from his account and drove around to every surf shop until he found a used nine-six gun that he bought for 600 dollars, more for the bright red color that anything else. He placed the gun into his dilapidated mini van and headed to the North Shore.

A big winter swell was peaking as he approached Haleiwa and his heart nearly stopped to see power walls collapsing and white water chocking off the harbor. It had been over thirty years since he had first seen those waves, but it all came back now, as fresh as sliced pineapple. Every place was closed out, all the way to Waimea Bay.

Waimea had a slight sideshore wind, but it was rideable, capping outside, and breaking in sets of three or four. It wasn't perfect, but it wasn't crowded. He took a quick look, parked the car, slammed one of the beers he had brought with him, and decided to paddle out.

His gut sagged far over the waistband of the dwarfed black trunks. The red board looked ridiculous beneath his arm, like a big red dart threating to punch a hole in an overfilled bag of mayonnaise. To the locals he wasn't even worth laughing at–just another dumb haole about to learn a lesson.

Joe made a bad show of stretching in the sand, an exercise that lasted less than a minute. He rehearsed a mental drill a friend had once suggested– "When you get hit by a big one, count one-one thousand, two-one thousand, three-one thousand, etcetera. That way you'll realize that even the worst wipeouts only last about fifteen seconds."

It wasn't what they call "real Waimea," a phrase that meant the entire Pacific Ocean had backed up and was about to cave in on you, all at once. It was what the locals called twelve to fifteen feet, the type of waves that offered a decent surfer a decent chance of making the drop and gliding safely into the channel, or being ground up by white water

Any first year psychology student could have pegged the symptoms as mid-life crisis. A textbook case if ever there was one. But Joe was not conscious of anything except that he always wanted to ride the Bay, and this was his day to do so.

The waves were gentle looking from shore, backing off quickly after what appeared an easy drop. Here was a wide channel, and he could get out of there in a hurry when needed. A few puffy clouds cut into the paper-blue sky, making the waves look all the more friendly. He waited, plopped into the shorebreak and paddled out without getting his hair wet.

From the water the surf looked a lot bigger and meaner than it had from shore. He sat quietly on the shoulder, silently daring himself into doing the bravest thing he could think of, which was simply to sit and watch and stay out through the next set.

He stayed out for two hours, watching great surfers take great drops, while he dodged the sets in the channel. Once he paddled into the lineup with the idea of taking off on a small "Pinballs" wave. He paddled for it, and backed out at the last second, after it steepened. By the time the next set arrived, his courage had plunged, and he flailed back into the channel with his head down so he would not have to face the monsters coming from the deep.

That set was at least two feet larger than the last one. The next set rose even more. By the time he decided to go in, the swell had jumped another four to six feet, the formerly clear water in the channel now a mass of thick, brown foam. This was real Waimea. The next set feathered in deep water and capped in the middle of the bay. He followed the others who paddled out to sea as he prayed to God. He prayed earnestly, in the way he had when he was a young altar boy, repenting of every bad thing he had ever done, not opening his eye to see the horror that was about to descend upon him.

There was no easy way out. The waves rolled in one continuous set now, and he moved further outside, praying for deliverance. One by one the other surfers caught smaller waves and left the water. Now, he was out alone, a camouflaged dot against a confused sea.

The wind kicked up to a hard onshore as the bright day went suddenly black beneath the shadow of the approaching wave. Everything was veiled behind the coming evening. That's when he faced the first closeout set that threw a net of water all the way across the North Shore.

In his many years as a surfer, Watterson had never seen anything like this. Comparing this to the biggest waves he had ever ridden was like comparing the flames of hell to the heat of a car with the windows rolled up. This was hell, and there was no way out of it. If his senses had not been on overload, he would have screamed out in terror. Instead he sat stupefied, watching a mountain range arrive from the north.

He would need all his strength to get back to shore, but he could barely lift his arms any longer. A black hand creased the horizon and touched him. A natural disaster as powerful as a tornado was focused on his soft body.

The newspapers would report that a middle-aged man had died attempting large surf. But they, nobody, could comprehend what had really happened out there. While he could not touch the big picture, the small details held his attention completely.

He had forgotten to count, and he had no idea how long he was under water. His thoughts rolled out before him like a newsreel as life went out of him and something else took hold. Suddenly he was up, looking at the ironic symbols of life and death–the church on the hill and the sacred beauty of Waimea Valley where, beyond sight, ancient Hawaiian warriors lay buried.

The next wave came at him like an iron horse. Its dark power hypnotized and then paralyzed him. He let go of terror for long enough to see the mountain as beautiful. Objectively speaking, it was the most beautiful thing he had ever seen. It was almost funny really– the most beautiful thing in the world was about to kill him. Like a man forced to drink molten gold, he would die from what he loved most. Part of him was too happy for words. The greater part of him was too terrified for anything. This was the stupidest things he had ever done, the smartest thing he had ever done. Right when he was about to die he had found a reason to live. He laughed loudly, with nobody to hear him.

There was a muffled crash when the forty-foot wave collapsed in the safety of the channel, one hundred feet in front of him. Watterson made an adrenaline-charged dive and managed to get fairly deep. In so doing, he avoided some of the impact. Still, he could feel forces more powerful than any he had ever imagined trying to destroy him. He was being tumbled to a depth unknown. A long, lonely darkness made darker because his eyes were tightly shut, swallowed him whole. That darkness was not his friend. It hated the old and the unprepared, the greasy french fries and beer.

The rat had taken the bait and barely had the will the resist the trap any longer. Then he remembered to count–one, one thousand, two, one thousand… It took all of his willpower and seemingly an eternity to get past three. He would never make it to fifteen! He had to breathe. Breathe. Claw for the surface, wherever that was. Time, he soon realized, was meaningless beneath this much water.

With his eyes still riveted shut, the light broke through. Water and sky lit up his world. It was his first day surfing, the type of red-letter day that separates life from lesser life. He was eleven-years old, and dragging his nine-six Hobie, purchased used for seventy-five dollars from his Dad's friend Harold, through the sand. The board was yellowed and cracked with age, but it was beautiful to him. Everything was beautiful. The doors of his life had been pried open just far enough to see that he would surf forever.

Surfers turned, kick stalled, hung five and ten. They did head dips, spinners, and drop-knee cutbacks. They did crazy and funny things too. Nothing in his life compared to the admiration he felt for these people. The sting of many dawns and the warmth of many sunsets stimulated and comforted him.

David Nuuhiwa was the best surfer then. For years David ruled from the nose, just like Donald Takayama had before him, and Rabbit Kekai before that. David didn't just get to the nose, he surfed there, rode it with tall elegance, like silk, like water, like the wave a string makes when you roll it out over a carpet. Five, ten, heels. Anything was possible.

Then, like a big dog tromping through a manicured flowerbed, Nat Young came along and pissed on our wet dreams. What could we say? The magazines said he was the best and maybe he was. They also said that noseriding was dead. Being young and too foolish to fight back, we believed them. We zealously cut the hearts from T-banded ten foot, three-stinger models. Fool's toys, we thought, in our media induced stupors. Laminated tailblocks and seventeen piece wooden masterpiece fins were all fuel for the baby and bathwater revolution.

In 1973, some of the longboards that had survived the ash heap were pulled from rafters and picked up at garage sale for ten bucks. Syd Madden had a battered Surfboards Hawaii Model A, and hung ten in the twilight at Swami's. Later that year Takayama made Watterson a cool new eight footer from an old Nuuhiwa template. David and Donald were back. So were Dobson and Herbie. No, they never left. Then, Nat came along again.

When he finally made the surface, Joe pushed away some of the slushy foam and chocked down the rest. He could breath. Barely. Instinctively he felt it—another wave, every bit as big as the last one was about to fall on him. If he survived this wave there would be others. He was being swept down the beach near the rocks where certain death awaited. That didn't matter anymore. He knew now that death was nothing. After a few good breaths, his oxygen-depleted high subsided and fear blanketed his world. An electronic current tore through his body. When he tried swimming toward shore his unstrung puppet hands barely ruffled the water. He saw the two pieces of his board being retrieved from the sand by a Hawaiian kid who looked out to sea without spotting Joe bobbing beyond the lineup. Meanwhile, Joe was being dragged further out to sea as the ocean prepared to mount a new charge against him.

Nobody realized he was out there, and those left on the beach packed up coolers filled with half-eaten sandwiches and empty beer cans. Once in the shade of evening, they covered themselves after dying all day from the poisonous sun. Fashionable ignorance, not big surf was stalking them.

The approaching wave rolled beneath him and lifted him a

full forty feet before it broke fifty yards inside of where he treaded water. He had been pulled a long way from shore and watched six-ty-foot plumes of spray shoot into the air. Joe, who now offered no resistance, was led like a newspaper boat in the gutter, further be-yond shore. There, he met a wave so tall and dark it was impossible to know where it ended and the sky began. He didn't dive down this time, but lay on his back, waiting to be crushed. When the power hit him, he went tumbling down, limbs flying every direction. Shock and adrenaline numbed the quick shoulder dislocation. When he had fallen all the way down the violent well, he landed in that peace-ful feeling again.

There had been talk that style was dead. That's when he saw the kid, a skinny boy of twelve, playing in the Cardiff shorebreak. This kid could hang ten all day long, if he wanted. This was new hope born into a nervous, chaotic world that had lost its way. But the grunt and wiggle brigade was not far off. They bounced through soup and did little flicks, head fakes and springboard airs on granny rockered thrusters they called longboards. Longboarding had returned, but many longboarders had forgotten something–something Rick Irons, Denny Tompkins, Stanley "Savage" Parks and Paul Strauch knew all about. "The best surfer in the world is the one having the most fun." Phil Edwards said that. "Surf 'til you die." Joe once said that.

A tribe of dark skinned, ancient people with wooden surf-boards reached out to him. These were the surfers who had ridden waves when time began. He somehow felt connected to this pow-erful chain. The chain gave him strength. He saw the tortured souls of precocious Malibu surfers. He rode their boards and shared their waves. He was the best. The worst. The winner. The loser. They adored him. They spat upon him. There were parties and girl and dangerous drugs and death. Then came the bulldozers to plow the world under as the god mammon rose again.

The magazines called it soul, but to name it was a lie. It had nothing to do with black wetsuits, Ray Ban Sunglasses, competition bands, cords or no cords. It had everything to do with how it felt when you rode a wave, not how it looked to someone else. It was surfing as if you were the last person on earth. Who would do a spinner or a headstand if nobody were watching?

"Ever watch a pelican glide?" Skip Frye asked that once. The way Frye blended with a wave was so pure that it was sometimes difficult to detect anyone on it. There were no disfiguring incisions left on the face. Move with the water. Let the wave move you. Don't force it. Let it happen. That was the key. The iron-hard water carried with it enlightenment.

He drifted and spun and remembered old friends: Harry Sonada, Cippy Cabatto, Tom Padaca, Ron Sizemore, Dale Struble, Mickey Madden, Cheer Critchlow, Gary Cooke, Gary Brummett, Jon Close, Jojo Perrin, George Mercal, Freddy Phaler, Tom and Bob Leonardo, Joey Hamasaki, Joyce Hoffman, Margo Godfrey, Kent Hollworth, Bill Fury, Tiger Espera, Darryl Diamond, Crazy Kate, Chris Marsalis, Chuck Erikson, the Lennahan's, Mark Martinson. They went through the Huntington Pier on big days. They rode Killer Dana, Long Beach Flood Control, Toes Over, and Garbage Hole before those spots were entombed behind breakwaters. The first time he hung five. Entering a contest. Winning a contest. Losing a contest. He could not even tell you where the trophy was. It was everything– for fifteen minutes. From then on it was dead metal, or more likely, plastic. It was all clear to him now. More clear than anything had ever been. He had been dead for years. Now, he was coming to life again.

A small white light broke in the distance. He went toward the light, and it made him feel as if he were floating without a body. The word heaven creased his lips. He felt an unpleasant pressure on his chest, as if something were trying to pull him back into the other world. He resisted going back, however, and continued toward the light.

Joining him on his journey were Dickie Cross and Bob Simmons. They each took a hand, and Joe grasped them tightly. He began to cry. The light was bright and clear now. And the light was the light of the world.

# Behold

In the dark, on the wet grass of Waimea, a large Samoan paramedic attempted pounding life into bloated flesh. He put his mouth onto the gray lips with the hope of starting the fallen man's heart. When nothing happened, he and two other men covered the body with a sheet, loaded it into the wagon and drove slowly away, telling jokes as they drove to keep themselves from remembering that their own time would come.

Cross and Simmons and Joe drifted above the Bay, and then floated peacefully above the violent water which lay before them like a path of molten glass.

The three spirits hovered above the water for a long time, and then moved out over the sea. Joe saw great whales, sharks and dolphins along with fish of all types. When the three men finally came to the end of the ocean, they moved easily upward, into a current of warm air.

Joe and his guardians made thousand-mile turns on invisible waves as they left the galaxy. Each turn brought greater understanding and joy. From high above he could see that the entire universe was one big wave, and he rode the power without hesitation, without effort, letting it happen. He encountered friends along the way, and they too rode, not competitively, but with soul and love. He lived in the pure happiness of an eternal wave, and let out a shout of joy that echoed throughout the wondrous light and sacred darkness for hours. He was not sure where he was going, but by now, I'm sure he has nearly arrived.

# THE ARK

*In the early 1970s Byron Bay in New South Wales, Australia, was being converted from a farm town to a surf town pioneered by wandering surfers. Arriving there with nothing but a surfboard, I was taken in by some Palos Verdes refugees. The wind and the rain could pound, but for two dollars a week we had shelter from every storm.*

–Originally published in *Good Things Love Water*

A streak of golden light hovered just above the heat lines on the black road like a 2,000-pound, extraterrestrial canary. Blasting through the eucalyptus forest, the streak twisted and mashed its way toward me before slowing down and coasting to the shoulder where I stood hitchhiking south from Noosa Heads to this place I had recently heard of, Byron Bay. The spaceship turned out to be nothing more than a 1966 Dodge Dart. The operator rolled down his window, and stared blankly in my direction, his concrete-blond pompadour pointing like a hunting dog to the south.

I sought instruction from him, but he remained as still as a porcelain Elvis. When I asked where he was going, he simply motioned down the road with his big, hard hair. Assuming he was offering a ride, I loaded my board into the car, threw my pack into the back seat, and climbed aboard. He took off like a shot, pinning me to the seat. Then he checked his watch and let out the first words I had heard from him, "One hundred kilometers in one hour." With that he tromped down on the gas pedal and bent the laws of physics all the way to the Brisbane. He skidded and swerved through the Gold Coast as I hung on tightly. He rarely slowed down and never muttered a word to me, but continued driving with dedication to some unspoken cause, which seemed somehow related to space and time. He checked his watch again and said, "One hundred kilometers in one hour."

Relieved by the sight of good surf, I asked to be dropped off at a point break I recognized as Kirra. He pulled over, I thanked him for the ride, and he addressed me for the first time. Flicking his sunglasses up until they rested on his forehead he smiled extended his hand for shaking and said, "If you ever get to Mullumbimbi, you tell 'em you met the Dart." He peeled down the highway and was once again nothing but a streak on the pavement.

Kirra was a good four-foot, and its best surfer, Michael Peterson, was out, moving his metronome arm to hold a tempo nobody else could keep. I surfed for two hours and came in only because I was hungry. It started raining before I had even dried off, and wanting to make Byron before nightfall, I again attempted hitching a ride. This time I was lucky to be picked up by a nice little family: a man, a woman and a teenaged girl, in a recreational vehicle.

The driver, a soft-spoken middle-aged dinky die Aussie, introduced himself as Colin. A middle-aged woman, whom I figured incorrectly for his wife, was ironically named Sheila. The teenaged girl introduced herself as Janet. They were away on holiday, or so I thought. I would eventually learn they were unrelated, and had met only weeks earlier at the mental institution they had escaped from in Brisbane. The RV, it turns out, was stolen, and they had been searching the New South Wales coast for a hiding place and some good, twisted fun.

We drove through Byron and Colin pulled in just south of town, at Broken Head Caravan Park. The rain suddenly hit like hammers as the water rose around us, and Colin found a level spot to stop and walked outside as Janet and Sheila retreated to the back of the RV and returned quickly, giggling and wearing nothing but silk panties. Janet snuggled up near me and said, referring to Colin, "He's bonkers mate." Sheila nodded in agreement, hung her crying head and said, "He scares me."

Holding the keys to the RV out to me, Janet begged me to drive away while Colin was out. I replied with stunned silence, looked out the window and considered sleeping outside in the downpour.

Suddenly Colin burst into the RV and stood tall before us, cradling a .22 caliber rifle. He grabbed Sheila by the hair as Janet hid behind me, clutching my ribcage. "Mongrel," shouted Colin at me. "I give you shelter, and this is how you repay me! You want my women; well take them." With that he grabbed Sheila and pushed her in my direction. The women were cowering now and trying to hide their nakedness with their hands. I shut my eyes and prayed silently. The steel of the rifle rested on my temple and I froze, praying and waiting impatiently to be transferred to the next world. Then–*click*–and loud laughter as the women poured themselves around Colin, holding and kissing him passionately.

"You're luck's changed, Mate," said Colin, pushing Sheila toward me as if she were a pair of old shoes he no longer wanted. I pushed her aside, grabbed my pack and my board and ran from the caravan through shin-high water, listening to their fading laughter as I fought the running water, trying to distance myself from my captors. Thankfully, they never came after me.

Sheets of rain fell from a black sky as I stumbled frantically, hoping I was free from them for good. I continued tromping through the mud, but was generally unable to grip the earth beneath my feet. Falling repeatedly, I continued moving forward in a wet, muddy daze. Unfamiliar with the area, I wandered for an hour or so, until, with no place left to go, I approached the door of the first habitat I saw–a large, rundown wooden shed with a rusty water tank attached to it.

A bearded man answered the door, and gently invited me inside. "Have you had your tucker, mate?" He asked as I stood, covered in mud on the warm dirt floor. Before I could reply, he had my coat hung up on a wooden peg. Excusing himself, he returned with a pair of dry overalls, which I changed into. He then took me to a rectangular room with a wooden picnic table in the midst of it. There sat two surfers of about my age, both with long hair and beards, slurping bowls of something that looked to be soup without looking up. They moved aside without comment, and I squeezed in beside them to devour fish stew and red wine poured into a fruit jar from a larger, chipped fruit jar.

The man who had come to the door was named Dave. He introduced me to Brian and Bill, who once they had eaten, wiped the crumbs from their beards and offered hospitality equal to Dave's. They were all three surfers from the U.S., drawn first to Sydney, then to Byron Bay because of its warm climate and good, uncrowded waves.

They never asked me about myself, but fell into a conversation that I soon found was perpetual among them, about surfing, their vegetable garden, and women, which, because of their isolation they had no close encounters with in six months. After a lively game of Crazy Eights and more wine, I was shown to a corner of the front room and given a blanket. I slept like death that night as the rain invaded my pleasant dreams by keeping rhythm on the tin roof.

The day broke sudden and bright blue, as I gazed from the window onto rolling green hills that ended in a long point wave. Dave wandered in and put a cup of hot tea into my hands, which I gratefully took. Crouching near my bed, he looked around at the old wooden structure, planted a hand on a beam, breathed deeply and said affectionately, "Ah, the Ark." He raised himself and, looking reverently at the tall beams, continued. "This place was an abandoned barn when Brian, Bill and I found it and turned it into our home." He paused before turning to me with a stern admonishment. "You've got to keep the doors closed when you're away or one of the older goats from the hills will wander in. They still think it's their home, poor bastards."

Continuing, Dave spoke like a friendly tour guide. "We call it the Ark because it survived the great flood last year, when water on the road was as high as a horse's mane," he said, holding his arm level with his chest to show just how high the water was. He continued looking lovingly at the dilapidated barn for a moment, and then stopped as if he had forgotten what he had originally come to say. "Breakfast is ready if you want any," he said before walking away.

I found my way outside where oatmeal steamed in a large metal pot beside a pitcher of fresh, cold milk and a variety of wild berries. We ate on a wooden bench beneath a sky that was too bright to look upon for long. Drops of water spilled from the leaves of one of the many eucalyptus trees. Quiet conversation consisted of swell direction and low tide, and punctuated by hundreds of lorikeets that crowded near the table for whatever scraps might fall.

We piled into Dave's old Holden FJ and rolled down a dirt track to one of Australia's most beautiful beaches where long, fast waves peeled around a point, or what I would learn Australians call a headland. "It'll be good today," said Dave unhurriedly while glancing casually at the ocean. The surf was good and far better all day, and the next, and for many days in a row after that.

Nobody ever offered it, but after a week it seemed I was an accepted tenant of the Ark. One morning Dave approached to say, "We've got a problem, mate." I figured I had been voted off the Ark and wondered where I would go next.

"Mate," Dave repeated, putting a sympathetic hand on my shoulder, "we're two months behind on rent, and we're all gonna get the boot. The rent's two bucks a week, plus a dollar a month for utes. That means we owe the old man…" He paused to figure up the sum in his head, then slowly raised his wooly head and said, "Eighteen bucks!"

I walked to my backpack and pulled out my last twenty, which I turned over to Dave. Not a man used to such miracles, he did nothing but stare at the bill for a moment. Next he felt it with his fingers, as if examining it to see if it was real. Finally he laughed loudly, and held the bill between his thumb and forefinger as he jumped up, shouting out, "We're saved! We're saved!" The boys gathered round to see the miracle of the twenty, before taking turns hugging me warmly.

The next day after surfing perfect six-foot barrels all morning, Brian was asked to walk to town to pay the rent. He had gone only a fraction of the ten kilometers when Officer Shales, the middle-aged town cop observed his long hair swaying in the breeze and pulled over. Shales offered him a ride, and Brian happily jumped into the front seat, knowing the cost of the ride would be a speech. "Now, Brian, you know I don't like hippies, but you and your mates seem okay to me. If you were a good bloke though, you'd cut your hair and get a job." Brian, who desperately wanted to be thought of as a "good bloke," promised to cut his hair and go to work. He then offered to shout Officer Shales a beer at the pub.

Although on duty, there was nobody to stop him, and so Shales and Brian became the talk to the town, walking into the pub together. Later that evening Shales' cop car came weaving up the dirt road to the Ark. He stopped, honked his horn and waved to us, as Brian came bounding up the drive wearing a flattop, just like the one worn by the officer. We helped Brian to the kitchen, placing the rent receipt hanging from his shirt pocket and the open gallon of wine in his hand onto the table.

Because of the vegetables they grew and the fish they caught, food was never a problem at the Ark. Wine, on the other hand, was not something we saw every day, although we would have liked to. The receipt said, "Paid: $13.00 for back rent. The remainder to be paid a week from today."

Bill and Dave took turns nipping from the bottle while I addressed the rent problem. They were all polite as I spoke. When I finished speaking, they were silent before Dave said I had a gift for public speaking. Brian and Bill nodded their heads in agreement and lifted their wine-filled fruit jars to me. They were too happy to speak about trivial matters like rent now and spoke instead about Brian's fine new haircut and how they all wanted to get one as soon as they had any money. Being warm and fed with a full bottle of wine to drink, all was well.

The next morning Brian awoke early to wax and comb his

new flattop. He liked the new look, but seemed upset by something. "I promised Officer Shales I'd get a job," he said, when I asked why he was unhappy. "Don't do it," said Bill, who overheard our conversation.

Brian thought for a moment, with the silent recognition that Bill had a point. Then he began speaking, "Yesterday Officer Shales and I become mates, and after I got me haircut, he said I was like a son to him."

The boys then knew the vow was serious, but they had no idea of how to solve Brian's problem. Brian was handy at many things, but he hadn't had a steady job for over a decade, not since he got fired from his paper route at twelve-years-old. There were few jobs in Byron Bay, but Dave read aloud from the want ads of a month-old local paper anyway.

"Barman wanted," he read.

"It's no good," said Bill. "He'd give all the piss away to anyone that lacked twenty cents for a beer.

"Here's another one for a deck hand on a fishing boat," said Dave, brightly, answering himself by saying that Brian was too kind-hearted to kill larger numbers of fish. Brian nodded and sat with his head in his hands, as one by one every job in town was eliminated for him.

Within a week a new swell helped Brian forget all about employment. It was time to pay the rent, however, and nobody had any money. A month later there was an evacuation notice nailed to our door.

I had lived in the Ark for six months and had never known anyone there to have a job. One night Dave called a meeting. The boys looked sad, the way they did whenever the surf went flat. Dave began somberly, "One of us is going to have to get a job, even if it's in the flower fields." Bill ducked his head shyly, as if not being seen would keep him from work. Brian sat, eyes wide, while remembering his promise to his mate, Officer Shales. "I'll go," he finally said, heroically sacrificing himself.

"No," said Dave to Brian, abruptly. "Whenever we have an

emergency, we do things the democratic way. Dave held out four straws in his hand. After we had all picked one, he lowered his head in defeat. His was the short straw. Feeling that Dave was troubled, I offered to accompany him to work the next day. Brian and Bill also said they'd go along, out of a sense of duty.

We worked together picking flowers for eight hours that day. By day's end we received about ten bucks cash each for our labor, and headed directly to the pub where we drank up much of our profit by shouting beers to the other patrons before buying a case of DB Beer to bring home.

Brian and I worked four more days and took home a total of fifty dollars each for our time. We paid the back rent, and I bought a green corduroy shirt in town for four dollars while Brian and I split the cost of a case of beef stew and a case of DB's.

It was Friday night and Ian, a local surfer who lived up the road from us, was going to the Cabbage Patch, a nightclub in the town of Coolangatta, twenty miles or so up the road. When he asked us to accompany him, I ironed my Levis with the heated water bottle we used for such purposes and wore them along with my new shirt. Brain also wore his new shirt while Dave and Bill pulled out moldy dress shirts and pants from cardboard boxes and put them on.

Dave cast an envious eye on my shirt as we entered Ian's Holden and headed to the Patch. Having been away from women for so long, we were a little awkward until we had a few beers in us. Brian was the first to make a move. He asked twin sisters, whose eyes were painted with big white stars around them to dance. They accepted and Brian danced with both of them while Bill danced shyly alone in the corner. Dave found a nice woman to dance with, but released her when her husband arrived. I ate alone at the table until a cute, short girl with straight blond hair asked me to dance with her. I introduced her to Dave and he kissed her hand, pulled at my corduroy shirt and angrily whispered in my ear, "Damn capitalist." I had never before heard him utter a word in anger and figured it was the alcohol talking.

# The Ark

The girl's name was Karen, and I asked Ian if we could drop her at her house in Coolangatta on the way back to Byron. "No worries, mate," he said as we piled into the car. Ian then passed out in the back seat, and Karen sat on my lap. Dave grabbed Ian's keys from his motionless hand and began the drive back to the Ark. With one hand on the wheel, Dave kept looking back to see what Karen and I were doing. I warned him repeatedly against oncoming traffic, and he mumbled something about my new shirt, before turning around again. I was kissing Karen when we came to an abrupt stop.

It wasn't so much a crash as a loud thud, and the left-front fender and the tree had become one. Karen was crying in my arms, and Dave, who sat in the front seat with the engine still running looked at me and said, "Well Matie, thanks to that shirt, I just hit a tree."

Dave worked for weeks alongside Brian, while Bill and I surfed or fished. Within a week, however, Bill and I became bored by the repetitive perfection and so joined the others at work. On the very day Dave paid off Ian for repairing his car, he quit working.

We all tried acting as if nothing had changed, and attempted to return to our old ways at the Ark. But things would never be the same. Bill and Brian had discovered work and with it items like wristwatches and flannel pajamas. And so they spent every weekday working. Dave said there was no hope for either of them.

I worked for a solid month and missed the best winter swell to hit Byron in a decade because of it. Bill and Dave hung out together whenever there was free time, and Brian hung out with Officer Shales, having dinner with him and his wife every Sunday night.

"Dave, what's become of the Ark?" I asked one evening as the sun set and we sat alone in the tall grass while he smoked a hand-rolled cigarette.

"Capitalism," he said. It all began with that shirt. You know you never would have gotten Karen if you hadn't been wearing it. It's a bloody shame to see this disease infect you and now Brian and Bill." Dave's words cut deeply. I walked out to the fading light and wandered over in view of the headland where I sat alone, remembering my narrow escape in the caravan half a year ago. Watching the long walls peel perfectly along the sandbar, I contemplated all I had traded for things of greater value than money. Dave was right.

When I returned to the Ark that evening, I reached into my pack, pulled out my folded green shirt, and offered it to Dave. He put his hands on my shoulders, looked me squarely in the eyes and took the shirt to the woodstove where he triumphantly tossed it into the fire.

Brian, meanwhile, was seated at the kitchen table reading a Police Academy book loaned to him by Officer Shales. He looked up just long enough to say he was leaving the Ark and applying to the academy, in Sydney. I wished him well and then went to my corner of the house where I lay, eyes wide open, long into the night and feeling alone.

The next day I awoke early, and walked to see that a powerful new swell was pouring deep, even lines into the headland. For the first time in months the four of us surfed together, riding waves deep in the pocket for hundreds of yards. That evening Brian officially revealed his plan to become a police officer. When it became evident there was no talking him out of it, Dave said we were going to have a party.

I took all my money from my backpack, went to the meat works and ordered half a pig. Bill picked all the corn from the garden and ordered a keg from the pub. I bought Brian a card and a green corduroy shirt with a ten-dollar bill hidden in the pocket.

The night before the party we all pitched in to dig a pit and placed the pig in it. The corn was roasted, the keg tapped, and we cleaned and decorated the Ark with crape paper streamers. A local group of musicians played some decent rock n' roll covers. There had never been such a party in the Ark, and surfers drove down from Noosa and up from Sydney to attend. Girls, including Karen came from all over the Gold Coast. Hippies came out of their communes and even Officer Shales and his wife arrived to eat, drink and dance in honor of Brian, who had the first dance with Mrs. Shales.

Brian rotated partners, and eventually settled on Karen. He was wearing the new corduroy shirt, and I realized Dave had been right all along. Dave, who could see that I was a bit hurt by losing Karen, offered me a conciliatory beer. By midnight we had eaten all the food and drank all the beer. When Ian left and returned with three gallons of wine, the party continued until dawn and sprawled out for two more days. People camped out on the grass near the Ark, and we feasted on fish and vegetables and played guitars while telling lies about the big waves we had ridden.

Brian walked to town where he took the bus for the Police Academy early the next morning. It took a full month before all of our guests finally went home. Gradually, however, things returned to normal–surfing, fishing, and drinking whatever wine we had. About a month later we received a letter from Brian saying he was happy and at the top of his class.

Every month or so, Dave would call a meeting to sadly announce a new financial crisis. Then one of us would sacrifice ourselves to the flower fields for a week or so, being extra cautious not to fall into the evils of capitalism again.

Just before I left the Ark and Australia to return to the States, a bewildered young Kiwi named John stumbled into the house during a rainstorm, looking for a place to stay. Dave put his arm on the lad's shoulder, welcomed him in his saintly fashion and gave him two words of advice. The first was not to become a capitalist. The second was to keep the doors closed whenever he was away. You never knew when some confused old goat might wander in, remembering that it had been his home a long time ago.

*Like most surfers they knew how to start things and not stop them,
and the train rattled and hummed until it ran out of fuel, on the
far side of the border.*

# NEXT TIME
# TAKE THE TRAIN

*Vicky Tuten was a good girl, ambitious, curious, fun loving. A seventeen-year old surfer from Belmont Shores, she would carry her board to the jetty and paddle to Ray Bay, that stingray-infested river mouth where she met friends like U.S. Surfing Champion Jack Haley. Noting her intelligence and honesty, Haley gave the girl a job, and she was soon managing the champ's surf shop in Seal Beach. When Haley and his team took surf trips, it was usually by car. Only once did they decide on a different mode of transportation.*

–Originally published in *Kelea's Gift*

It was a hot summer day with a clean south swell running when Captain Jack decided to make a Trestle run. This would require enough stealth to beat the Marines at their own game. Jack, along with fellow surfers Eddie Brenner, "Wallpaper," Ernie Morgan, "Toes," and one of Long Beach Surf Club's founders, Vicky Tuten made their way through the Cotton's Estate, past the barbed wire, past the Point and Uppers, to Lower Trestles, just in time to watch solid six-foot lines turn to onshore mush as he afternoon wind began to howl.

Moving onward required a long and risky walk through enemy territory, laying low to avoid capture. On their way out they noticed that the train engine was stopped on the tracks and empty. The engineer must have been in the bushes, pissing. Also doing what came naturally, Haley climbed aboard and fiddled with the controls. Surfers and boards were loaded, and team Haley figured out how to make the big machine move forward, destination a mere half-mile away, at San Onofre. When they saw the wind had blown out Old

Man's they continued further to Mile Zero. Why not Oceanside?

And so the little engine began picking up steam, Haley at the helm chugging through Oceanside, Carlsbad and Del Mar where residents expressed shock to be mooned by the engineer and his five unruly conductors. Might as well check out Mexico. Like most surfers they knew how to start things and not stop them, and the train rattled and hummed until it ran out of fuel, on the far side of the border.

*Vicky Tuton continues to be an adventurous traveler, but usually drives cars to her destinations.*

Behold

# THREE
# NEW SURF STORIES

# ON FIRE

*Like so many of my stories, this one begins with me being broke and wondering how I would survive. The year was 1990, and I had just returned from a disastrous year in Australia. Upon my return it became obvious that longboarding was experiencing a great resurgence, and I wanted to make a surf film about it. I first told my friend Steve Walden the idea, and he liked it. Then I told another friend, Steve Cleveland, and he quickly found enough money to get us going. We hired surf filmmaker Greg Weaver, and I suggested two unknown up-and-comers to star in the movie along with established pros Skip Frye and Donald Takayama.*

With our budget secured, I borrowed my friend Johnny's van. The idea for the film was that two young, talented longboarders longed for the magical '60s and would meet up with their heroes Skip Frye and Donald Takayama. After painting Johnny's van '60s style on the street in front of Cleveland's house, he, Joel, Wingnut and I putted north to San Onofre to meet up with a cast of characters including surfing greats: Herbie Fletcher, David Nuuhiwa, Dale Dobson, and Phil Edwards. We were about half way to our destination, approaching Las Pulgas Road on Camp Pendleton, when fourteen-year old Joel Tudor squeaked out, "We're on fire!" At first I refused to believe it, but as the smell of smoke overpowered us, I was forced to pull over. After unloading our boards, we stood on the side of the road and watched Johnny's classic vehicle go up in flames.

Around that time Donald Takayama's nephew, Michael pulled over and offered us a ride to San Onofre. We arranged to have the car towed home and dropped into an afternoon of fun and little waves with blazing talent in the lineup. San Onofre was a blast with

*We were half way to our destination when fourteen-year old
Joel Tudor squeaked out, "We're on fire!"*

everyone buzzing about the up-coming film. After surfing, Donald barbecued swordfish; we ate and surfed to heart's content.

Joel and Wingnut put on a show, and Weaver's footage proved as artistic and inventive as ever. We didn't get much surf during subsequent days of filming. Still, with music donated by surf music pioneer Paul Johnson and film clips generously donated by Herbie Fletcher and Bruce Brown, the film *On Safari To Stay* proved a modest success and was, perhaps, the first longboard surf movie of modern times.

Joel and Wingnut went on to become international surf stars, with Joel winning two world titles and being unofficially crowned the best longboarder of his time. Wingnut spring boarded to a co-starring role in in an epic film with a far bigger budget than ours, Dana Brown's *Endless Summer Two*. Steve Cleveland became inspired, bought a video camera and went on to make several more classic surf films. Greg Weaver took his surfboards and cameras to Baja where he lives to this day. I went surfing, wrote stories about it, and edited the first longboarding magazine.

A torched van and a few million dead brain cells from worrying about such matters proved a small price for having such a great time and helping launch the modern longboard industry. Still, I'm in no hurry to ride along on a surf movie again. I've found it's safer to watch things burn from the sidelines.

# FATHER'S MEDALS

Mister Duff, our next-door neighbor displayed his Japanese flags, American bayonets, and the U.S. Army uniform he proudly wore to the parade every Veteran's Day every chance he got. We, the kids in the neighborhood, admired him greatly and never tired of hearing how he had killed many Japanese soldiers in hand-to-hand combat. Of course he never called them Japanese. To him they were forever "Japs." He had saved the world from them, so kids like us could know freedom. One afternoon when the war stories ended, he feed us chipped beef and gravy slopped over white bread–something he and other veterans called SOS. It tasted as bad as it sounded, so I took one bite, excused myself, walked toward home, and spat everything onto his rose bushes.

One Saturday afternoon he told us of a particularly hot battle where he was, as usual, the hero who killed everyone that dared to wear an opposing uniform. With the story finished, I ran home to ask my dad how many of the enemy (he would not tolerate us calling them Japs) he had killed on the destroyer escort where he served in the Great World War. "I never killed anyone," he said, frankly.

Not wanting to believe him, I pressed further. "What about the newspaper article that said you had been decorated for bravery?"

"They mistook me for someone else," he replied.

I settled into the idea that my father was a gentle coward. He couldn't have always been that way, however. As a young man he had surfed in and around Hermosa Beach with legendary surfers like the Kerwin brothers. He was mostly a swimmer then, and during Prohibition he and his buddies would swim from the Santa Monica Pier, out to the party boats parked three miles offshore. Once there, they would climb aboard, slam a drink or two and swim back to shore before dark.

He had quit surfing by the time we began, in the early '60s. Still, he would be up early every weekend to take my brother Dave and I and anyone else in the neighborhood who needed a ride, surfing. We loved him, not for his bravery, but for his kindness. Over the years some of our friends would fall on hard times, and it was always Dad who helped them out with a ride or a meal. When he died in the mid-1980s everyone who ever knew him was saddened by the fact.

It was more than a decade later when his youngest sister, Bea, was dying. My wife Tracy and I drove to Newport Beach to visit her. I had spent many happy days in that house in my gremmie years, drying off on the lawn after hours in the water, before eating Uncle Harry's double thick barbecued hamburgers. Aunt Bea, who was as kindhearted as her big brother, was always gracious and happy to see us. On that final visit, she wanted to talk, not about herself, but her brother, my father, the man she adored.

"You probably don't know much about him," she began, weakly.

"I do, we talked often," I replied.

"Did he ever tell you about the time the man was shot on the sidewalk in front of our house?" she asked.

"I never heard that story."

She said it had been a few years since their father had died. They, her older sister, my Aunt Dorothy, the middle child, my father, their mother Myrtle and the baby, Bea, herself were huddled up inside after a man was shot dead on the sidewalk, directly in front of their Los Angeles home. Bea explained how my dad, who was then twelve-years-old, took the family rifle from the wall, loaded it, locked the door from the inside, shut it behind him, and sat on the front porch rocker throughout the evening until the next morning, to protect the family.

Realizing there was far more to my father than the man I had grown up with, I asked to hear more about him. It was then she began the tale of how he had joined the Navy during WW II and used his powerful swimming abilities to rescue half a dozen men from freezing water after their boat had been torpedoed. Upon his return from the service, the family was proud of him. Aunt Bea in particular was curious and asked to see the medals he had earned for bravery. My aunt and I shared tears as she continued. "He told me he had thrown his medals overboard, saying, 'There's no glory in war.'" True to his kind nature, my father had saved lives, not taken them.

There are no medals to remember our father by, just the kindness forged in his heart that he extended to everyone he ever met.

As for Mister Duff, our next-door neighbor, I eventually discovered the truth about him. He had in fact been in the Army during the War. Turns out he worked as a mess cook, something only those brave enough to endured his meals could die from.

# RUNAWAY

The divorce parted him and his possessions as effectively as a house fire. It had been a year of post marital non-sex and fighting and now he lacked the energy to battle over the two cars, motorcycle and condo in that inland, gated community. The residuals of whatever love she once had for him would surely result in a fair settlement. Believing that, he surfed the first day of a crisp north swell rather than show up for court to defend himself. Having underestimated his spouse's determined bitterness he was left with two surfboards, his rebuilt VW van, his clothes, books, family heirlooms, and the family dog, a Chow named Diego.

Later that year life completely bottomed out with his father's death and the literal house fire that *did* burn his few remaining items to such fine ash that the wetsuit could not be differentiated from the alarm clock. With no job, no map and no plan, he woke early one morning, packed his boards, sleeping bag and Diego into the van, fueled up and pointed the vehicle north.

It was early November 1983 with a light rain falling as he pulled into a campsite in Big Sur and shared a cold can of beef stew with Diego in the fog. With all beauty barred from sight he could have just as easily been in Barstow. Hope of riding the secret reefs nearby vanished as he woke to a socked-in dawn before heading further north in the black mist. By midmorning he was riding the little wind swell that brought life to the reefs north of Santa Cruz. Packing up again he continued north, riding some thumping high tide wedges in San Francisco's generically named Ocean Beach. Solid waves north of the bridge and an infinite road expanded his thinking as mystery coves presented big-wave potential.

Several hundred more miles, an hour ferry ride, hours of logging road, and a downpour only Noah could appreciate, left him stranded amid tall trees and deep mud with nothing but a decent point wave peeling into an ice-cold river mouth to ease the pain. The setup was nice, but it would require more swell to club the anxiety bear that continued to claw at his brain.

That night while camping, he met the captain of the little skiff named Crystal Voyager. The captain had those telltale signs of being a *tweeker* in that he never quit tinkering on the Mercury outboard motor or speaking nonsense. For fifty bucks he would take him to a point he swore was every bit the equal of J-Bay.

On the boat ride there, they were threatened by powerful wind and surf that nearly capsized them. While terrifying to both passenger and dog, the captain laughed loudly before grinding down on his few remaining teeth. The point, that was on a Native American reservation showed promise but failed to reveal its best side in the drizzle and the mild onshore wind. When he asked one of the local tribesmen about hazards in the surf, the tribesman simply snickered and replied, "Sharky" before turning away. Yet somehow and somewhere in the cold and the mud of the moment, he lost his depression and anger and surfed something akin to a short, high tide onshore Rincon alone for four hours.

He avoided disaster and getting barreled in decent surf, and when boredom eventually hit, he crawled into the leaky tent provided for him by the captain. Once there he zipped himself into his sleeping bag and quickly located boredom's twin brother depression, which was only napping. Even Diego, who faithfully cuddled up at his feet, did nothing but increase his longing for home. The captain, who made camp for himself in the hull of the boat with a tarp overhead, smoked his meth pipe nervously, stacking and unstacking river rocks to build what he called "a rainbow bridge," while raving non-stop about everything from weather patterns to the mind control brought on by government cheese. He ended up paying the captain fifty extra bucks to get him out of there early. After a near-death experience in twenty-foot seas on the return boat ride, it was comparatively enjoyable to get the van stuck in the mud as he attempted driving back toward San Diego.

Time and again he would dig the wheels free, drive a few hundred feet, go into a four-wheel drift and get stuck. This went on for most of one day, until two lost surfers from Newfoundland rescued him by towing him out in their old four-wheel drive Jeep. To call them surfers was a great exaggeration; really–they had never surfed before but had made the worst surfboards imaginable from a *People Magazine* ad, and then driven the girth of Canada to get here. Painted on the deck of each board were the words "Feel the Pain." Crowning each wave steed was a leash consisting of a five-foot piece of yellow nylon chord with a hangman's noose on the passenger end, secured to the deck by a rusty deadbolt.

Together the trio managed to find decent surf on the island and the Newfie's (as people from Newfoundland are sometimes called) paddled out alongside him. The Newfies laughed and pearled and, without another surfer for miles, managed to run each other and him over. The big Newfie apologized and offered to repair the dinged board. He politely declined after re-examining the Newfie's craftsmanship. He couldn't be mad at either of them, however. These were some of the best surf companions he had ever encountered, ready for anything and wanting to surf whatever the ocean threw at them, which in the Pacific Northwest can be all anyone can handle.

Together they took on waves few sane people ever would. He kept an eye on the Newfies to be sure they didn't drown in the eight to ten foot steamrollers. Even he, prepared with twenty years experience and a 6'10" pintail that was pushed to its limit, was challenged by the conditions. Meanwhile his robust companions were having the time of their lives taking off and pearling before being dragged under water to the beach. "Feeling the Pain," for them apparently translated to great fun.

That evening they toasted their survival with coal fire burnt steaks, a lobster the little Newfie had taken from the shallows, and some local beers.  When he revealed that he was leaving for San Diego the next day, the big Newfie lowered his head sadly and said, "We don't want you to leave, but if you do we have a friend in Newport, Oregon where you can stay on your way home."

"She's a very nice girl and will be glad for the company," said the little Newfie before searching his little black book and copying Suzie's phone number onto a sheet of scrap paper. The surfers (the Newfies had in fact earned the title of surfer simply by their determination) had been together ridding waves for two weeks. December was days away, promising violent Aleutian storms that would thrash this coast for months.

He awoke early that morning attempting to depart without saying goodbye. As he pulled out of camp, Diego cried and clawed the van's passenger window while the driver made the mistake of looking into his rearview mirror to see his new friends, his brothers waving goodbye like children might a father marching off to war.

Horizontal rain and gusty winds rocked the van all through Washington State and well into Oregon. The sound of rain, which most native Southern Californians enjoy, was not quaint to him any longer, but echoed relentlessly like living inside a steel drum while someone dropped a million ball bearings on the lid.

He drove through the night before coming to the little town of Newport, Oregon. The rain was clearing but the drizzle remained, which it tends to do for months at a time. The wind blew hard onshore all that morning. With surfing or any other ocean activity out of the question, he reached into his pant's pocket, pulled out the number, found a phone booth and called Suzie.

Turns out this was the young woman's work number. She came to the phone and told him to come by the doctor's office front desk so she could give him her house key. Somehow in their description the Newfie's omitted that Suzie, who was herself proudly Newfie, was gorgeous, with light freckles, long, silky auburn hair and a gentle smile that penetrated the scar tissue of his broken heart for a moment. Not ready for relationship, however, he tried not to notice her appearance, simply said thank you and made his way to her house on the outskirts of town. *She might like me, and I might...* he thought, allowing himself to dream as he approached Suzie's house.

The house was fit for a Hobbit–small, tidy, wooden and set amid an old-growth pine forest with a river flowing through the backyard. To make the Rockwell scene complete, there was a red-wood barn located next to her house about a hundred yards below the steep gravel driveway. Anxious for a long nap, he stopped the van and opened the redwood gate that lay downhill in the tranquil paradise. Then, suddenly he felt a pressure being exerted on his back. The drive must have been more wearing than he thought. Turning around, he realized his back was not the problem, but something far worse was–the van was loose and rolling down against him after the emergency brake failed. No problem, really. The van was barely moving. He would simply quit trying to hold it back and run to the driver's door to open it. When he did, he found he had locked it.

Diego barked as the driver ran to the opposite side of the van as it gained momentum, and he grabbed the door handle. The side door opened, but the van was moving faster than he could run now, and he was too late to jump in. Digging his heels into the muddy gravel, he vainly tried to hold onto the van and keep it from rolling down the hill into the river. His fingers felt like they would come out of their sockets. With no option left, he released the door handle, watching in horror as Diego sat up, terrified, as the van gained speed, wobbling slightly and nearly falling over before it righted itself and made its way toward a watery grave. Achieving the ruts further down the driveway the van straightened out and made a direct line to the barn. Unable to bear the sight of his van plowing into her barn, he covered his eyes while the sound of the 100-year old structure that had weathered a century of storms met metal, and peace in the valley was disturbed.

He opened his eyes just in time to see timbers flying, the larg-est of them landing on the propane tank line a few feet from the barn. The line ruptured and made a faint hissing noise as the gas leaked into the otherwise pristine air. As inept as he was at any sort of handyman work, he knew enough to shut the propane valve. He then walked to the van, opened the door and released the happy Diego. The van was now firmly wedged in the barn all the way to the back door and immovable when he tried to back it out. Again and again he tried moving the van, but it would not budge.

Cell phones were about a decade away from common usage, and he was miles from town. He contemplated using the house key, but wanted to be in view when Suzie arrived, to help her settle into the idea that his van was lodged in her barn. With nothing left to do, he and Diego sat beneath the dripping eves of the house as mist turned to rain and then light snow that gently dusted the tall pines. It would have been so pretty under most circumstances.

To order signed copies of *Behold What Is Greater Than Thyself,* please send $20.00 (includes tax and S&H) to:
Perelandra Publishing Company
P.O. Box 697, Cardiff, CA 92007
Or through PayPal, to: perelandrapub@gmail.com

Other surf books by Chris Ahrens include, the surf story trilogy, including:
Good Things Love Water
Joyrides
Kelea's Gift
*These volumes are currently sold out.

To order signed copies of *Twilight in the City of Angels* in hard cover, please send $25.00 (includes tax and S&H) to:
Perelandra Publishing Company
P.O. Box 697, Cardiff, CA 92007
Or through PayPal: perelandrapub@gmail.com

Books can also be ordered through the Perelandra Website:
http://www.perelandrapublishing.com/


To order prints from Wade Koniakowsky Ocean Art, visit:
http://www.koniakowsky.com/


*"What kind of man is this? Even the winds and the waves obey him!"*

–Matthew 8: 27